PRACTICAL
OPERATIONS
MANAGEMENT

PRACTICAL OPERATIONS MANAGEMENT

Mike Hayes
Anne Tomes
University of Sheffield

PHILIP ALLAN
OXFORD AND NEW JERSEY

First published 1988 by

PHILIP ALLAN PUBLISHERS LIMITED
MARKET PLACE
DEDDINGTON
OXFORD OX5 4SE (UK)
and
171 FIRST AVENUE
ATLANTIC HIGHLANDS, NJ 07716 (USA)

British Library Cataloguing in Publication Data

Hayes, Mike
  Practical operations management.
  1. Project management
  I. Title II. Tomes, Anne E.
  658.4′04

ISBN 0−86003−558−1
ISBN 0−86003−658−8 Pbk

Library of Congress Cataloging in Publication Data

Hayes, Mike.
  Practical operations management.
  1. Production management. I. Tomes, Anne.
II. Title.
TS155.H349 1988   658.5   88−19368

ISBN 0−86003−558−1
ISBN 0−86003−658−8 (pbk)

Typeset by MHL Typesetting Limited, Coventry.
Printed and bound in Great Britain by the
Oxford University Press, Oxford.

CONTENTS

v

PREFACE

This book is aimed at students who have not studied operations management before.

In writing any book on operations management it is difficult to know what to put in and what to leave out: the subject is so vast. Most operations management textbooks available are very long American 'blockbusters'. This has two consequences. First, many students cannot afford to buy their own texts — an unsatisfactory situation. Secondly, those students who do buy such texts find that having worked their way through the 700+ pages, there is insufficient time (and inclination) to read other authors and get a different perspective.

It was our objective, therefore, to keep the length of this book down and to bring it within the budget of the average student.

We believe that students cannot learn about operations management solely from reading books. They need to conduct experiments, observe the results and draw conclusions as with all practical subjects. Our book therefore includes many exercises which simulate real and often complex operations management techniques. For example, students are encouraged to re-create Taylor's ingot-loading experiment to learn about work measurement. Quality control is also taught through a series of experiments, as are the differences between Push and Pull production systems.

The book includes contact exercises involving students in conducting interviews with practising operations managers, looking at various aspects of their organisations, picking out the problems and the good points, and discovering why these exist.

We try to present a basic grounding in operations management and aim to stimulate the student not only to read more widely but to go out and find out what is happening, which techniques are being used successfully and in what situations. We want to cultivate an analytical approach to operations management; we feel knowledge is not enough on its own.

Our objective has been to cover the major aspects of operations management in 250 pages. Obviously we cannot cover every aspect, nor can we deal in as much detail as we would have liked with those techniques in which we personally have a particular interest. Service, retailing, transport and manufacturing operations are considered. The jobs of various operations managers are looked at through their own eyes. Although we obviously cover nitty-gritty techniques such as day-to-day scheduling we take a holistic view of operations.

The product is looked at not only from the production viewpoint but also from that of the consumer and we devote a whole chapter to quality, now coming to its rightful place in the forefront of operations management.

Whether it be an iron-casting or a bank cash-card service, the machines and materials involved in producing the product are important and receive due consideration. 'People' are considered at length and in a variety of contexts. However automated an operation, its success in the long run depends on people. Operations, as systems, are then discussed − the concept of combining machines, materials and people into a working whole.

Forecasting is given a brief chapter. Not that this should be construed as a measure of how important we feel it is but because the topic is well covered in several texts which we recommend to the reader.

Our chapter on scheduling, though the longest in the book, can be no more than an introduction to a massive subject. Nonetheless we discuss the major techniques and provide exercises for the student to work on. Not only do we look at scheduling in on-going operations but we devote a chapter to the scheduling and implementation of one-off projects in which a computer-installation project and construction projects are discussed in detail.

To round off, we remind readers of the place of operations management in a business, how general-management decisions impinge on operations management and how seemingly insular operations-management decisions can have far-reaching effects for the organisation.

We give a small number of references to specialist texts at the end of each chapter. Also, the end of each chapter gives abbreviated references to standard operations management and case-study texts. Full details of these texts are given in the Bibliography at the end of the book, along with a brief review explaining which sections in each we recommend, and why.

We are indebted to many organisations, colleagues and students. Many organisations have contributed case-study material for which we are grateful. Many wish to remain anonymous but we thank them nonetheless.

We can thank by name Mr A.Grant of Clatterbridge Hospital, Mr S. Hellewell of South Yorkshire Transport Limited, Mr J. Salmon of the Halifax Building Society, Mrs D. Whittles of Sheffield Children's

Hospital, Mr P. Wilson of Pine Furniture Limited, and the Operations Research Executive Group of British Coal.

We are also grateful to Austin Rover, Deltacam, and Wilson and Longbottom for the provision of photographs.

Several colleagues and students have contributed to the exercises and case studies included in the book. We would especially like to thank Liz Andrew, Jo Brockway, Chris Eve, Fiona Franey, Harvey Gifford, John Hayes, Mark Hearn, Alison Heys, Marian Kay, Sau Ping Li, Pete McClusky, Julian Miller, John Mills, Tim Pickston, Ron Skuse and Chris Whitehead.

Our long-suffering typists Pat Fall, Elaine Hornbuckle and Sharon Rose deserve special mention. Our many revisions, despite word processors, must have tried their patience beyond the call of duty.

We must, of course, thank our families, Mary, Peter, Alison, John, Rosie and Jenny Hayes and Frank, Stephanie and Alexia Tomes without whose support this book would never have been possible.

Anne Tomes
Mike Hayes
University of Sheffield
April 1988

Chapter 1

THE SCOPE OF OPERATIONS MANAGEMENT

What is operations management?

Whenever we start a course, our students always ask that question. Operations management covers such a broad spectrum of activities that it is not always easy to answer in a few words.

Retail organisations, transport operations, manufacturing companies and service and leisure organisations all have operations managers. In a manufacturing company the operations manager is called the production manager, and is responsible for getting the company's product made to an agreed specification. In a transport organisation the term 'operations manager' is frequently used, meaning the person responsible for ensuring that the transport service runs to an agreed schedule and, in many cases, for setting those schedules. In a retail organisation the operations manager is usually called the store manager, and is responsible for pushing the merchandise through the store to the customers. In a service industry, the operations manager may have one of several titles, such as a branch manager in banks or estate agencies, and will be responsible for running his or her own unit, providing customers with an agreed service.

It is the job of all these operations managers to utilise their organisations' resources to meet their product or service specifications effectively. These seemingly diverse operations, therefore, do have similarities. Such a realisation has brought a management emphasis to higher-level operations jobs, rather than the technical emphasis prevalent, particularly in the production field, for many years. At last the idea is disappearing that the production manager must be capable of personally dismantling and rebuilding every machine in the factory. Operations are now being viewed in the context of the whole business, in the role of the supplier of the product or service required by the market place.

Some sectors recognised this sooner than others. In many ways this was due to the nature of a production operation as opposed to a transport, retail or service operation. In these latter operations the workforce is always aware of the customer. Customers are seen all day, every day, by sales staff on a retail shopfloor, or cashiers behind a window in a bank, or bus drivers on their daily routes. In all these cases a large percentage of the workforce is in constant contact with customers. In the case of the manufacturer this is not so. Ninety-nine per cent of the workforce will probably never see a finished product let alone a customer. The inward-looking attitude of manufacturers is therefore easy to understand. In Drucker's words, they may have been 'doing the operations side right', but they were not 'doing the right thing' and, no matter how efficient the operations side of the business, success has to be considered within the total business context.

Therefore, throughout this book we take a holistic approach to operations management. Of course we look at nitty-gritty problems of operations management like day-to-day scheduling — a vital area, involving such work as ensuring that there are enough cashiers at bank windows during the lunch hour, or performing a juggling act with several different customers' orders to try to utilise machines effectively whilst keeping to delivery-date promises. This is the role of the first-line operations manager and is vitally important for an efficient operation. However, the reason for the operation's existence can easily get forgotten in the struggle for an excellent manufacturing process or an elegant computer system. We must remember the operations function is there not to supply what we can produce in terms of goods or services but to provide what the customer wants, profitably in the case of a business, and within budget in the case of a local government or other non-profit-making organisation. To give you a feel for the scope of operations management, we have interviewed several successful operations managers involved in various types of business.

Operations Manager No. 1 — Department Store Manager

My job is to ensure that the several million pounds of merchandise in the shop at any one time moves through as fast as possible. In other words we are interested in increasing turnover. But we do this always bearing in mind the philosophy

Figure 1.1 Customer flow in a department store

behind our business. We have a trading policy which we always adhere to. First of all we must offer excellent value, a high level of service and a wide assortment of merchandise, and we always trade with absolute honesty. For example, we don't use small-print disclaimers found on some sales goods in some stores. I think you can see that such a trading policy means that we have to be internally very efficient. The Company collects a lot of statistics and we spend quite a lot of time examining our own navels.

There is competition between the branches and each week the percentage change in sales of each is published, not just within the Company, because outsiders can easily get this information as well by subscribing to our Journal. So you're really kept on your toes. If you're not performing, someone wants to know why. We break down this accountability to department level. Each departmental manager is reviewed on the progress of his department during the previous year. If one department is doing badly compared with a similar department in a different city I need to know why. There are sometimes good reasons. For example, a Boyswear Department is going to do better in a city with a younger population, where the Education Authority requires school uniform to be the standard, than in one with an older population where schoolwear is, shall we say, less formal. I take such things into account.

The policy of a high level of customer service extends across the board. If a customer writes a letter of complaint to me personally, then I answer personally. Incidentally, during the past year we received 138 complaints compared with 86 complimentary letters. I suppose with some six million customers a year that's not bad, but I would like us to do better. Having said that, I do occasionally have to take decisions in the interests of economics, which will upset a few customers. For example, I had to close the waitress-service restaurant recently. The tables were almost empty, whereas the self-service café was bulging at the seams and unacceptable queues were building up. So, to satisfy the silent majority, I have had to upset a very small minority. In fact I have had eleven letters of complaint, the most I've ever had on one subject. But the decision had to be made. On the other hand, the number of customers served increased by 500 in the first week. So we hope we have another 500 happy customers to balance those who were upset.

The essence of retailing is speed. For example, our central warehouse makes deliveries to us every day and on Friday afternoons. If we don't get that stock into the shop for Saturday morning, our biggest selling day, we risk running out of stock on fast-moving items and losing sales. This is where we try to get the lead on our other branches. If we don't move quickly enough the merchandise won't reach the selling floor until Monday or Tuesday; by then we should have sold a lot of last week's delivery and be re-ordering. So we get a fast turnover and also first call on the merchandise in Central Warehouse.

Stocking policy is a critical area in retailing. Broadly speaking, we know that about 20 per cent of our assortments (or lines) generate 80 per cent of our sales. So we work very hard to ensure we can keep that top 20 per cent continuously available and keep as much of the remaining 80 per cent in stock as seems reasonable. This keeps our stock levels down whilst satisfying the majority of our customers. Naturally, we can always get other items for a customer should we happen to be out of stock. We can ask another branch, for example, to send something over quickly, or we can put in an order quickly to the Central Warehouse.

Another important area of my work is looking at the customer flow through the shop. It is important for customers to be able to move around comfortably, without being jostled, when they are making for a particular department. But we would like to encourage them to look at other items on the way, and to make another purchase in addition to the one for which they came into the shop. For example, we used to have a 15 ft-wide straight walkway from the main entrance to the escalator. This meant that customers frequently didn't consider walking around the floor, but made straight for the escalators. So we shortened this walkway and introduced a Y-shaped walkway configuration. It is still possible to go straight ahead, but now the invitation is there to walk around the ground floor. Sales have improved since.

Another retailing headache is scheduling staff lunch breaks. At the busiest time in the day, one-third of our staff are on lunch break. We use part-timers who work over this 3-hour period but I don't think we have got the complete solution. I don't think anyone has, unless overlapping shifts are used and that would be costly.

We are interested in providing a good service, so we look at the queue lengths at the tills. We won't tolerate queues of more than four customers if we can possibly help it. To provide a no-queue situation we would need an uneconomic number of cash registers which would use up merchandising space and require many more staff. So our costs would go up, and prices would follow. We have got to keep a balance. The main thing is to make sure all the tills we have available are in operation when needed, and departmental managers are expected to ensure this happens.

Retailing is highly competitive and we have to give the customers what they want in terms of value and service. There is no room for compromise. But most of all we have to do it quickly!

Operations Manager No. 2 – Operations Director of a Public-sector Bus Operator

In a nutshell, we are in the business of selling movement for reward. The function of operations in the transport business is quite specific: we are there to deliver the service specification. In other words, if we promise there will be a bus leaving point A at 8.15 and arriving at point B at 8.30, then it's our job to ensure that that happens. With unlimited resources, of course, this job would not be too difficult. If we had plenty of spare buses and crews at different locations waiting to be called on whenever we needed them, many of our problems would disappear. But whether we are operating British Airways, or a fleet of supertankers, the key to an efficient and successful operation is to make sure that the capacity on offer mirrors the demand.

Too much supply incurs costs, too little supply causes irate customers and leads to a breakdown in the service which makes costs rise. So when we get estimates of demand, we have to match our capacity to that. Generally, if I were to give one rule of thumb, what we need to do is minimise 'light running'. In

Figure 1.2 London, Piccadilly traffic jam

other words, minimise the mileage our buses travel with no passengers between routes or back to the garage. We leave day-to-day scheduling in the hands of the garages with minimal central guidance. The minute-by-minute operation is in the hands of inspectors and the foreman.

To give you some idea of the size of the operation, we run 1000 buses, 360 days of the year, 7 days a week, 20 hours a day. So I must delegate. As it is I find that I often work one day at the weekend, and a few hours each evening, but I enjoy it. This extra work has really come about by massive changes in the provision of local bus services. Now the situation is settling down, and we are beginning to be able to concentrate on operating an efficient service in the new environment. I had better try to explain. The bus industry in the UK has now become deregulated. In other words, operators can run a bus service on any route as long as they give 42 days' notice of their intentions and have a valid Operators' Licence. So there is competition back in the bus industry. This hasn't been known since the 1930s, when road-service licensing regulations were first brought in to protect the public from competing cowboy bus operators who were not maintaining adequate safety standards. Deregulation has inevitably had a radical effect on our thinking. In addition, the metropolitan counties were abolished. This caused massive organisational changes. Not only this, but many councils were then rate-capped. This meant operators found that subsidies disappeared and we were forced to put up fares, in some cases by up to 250 per cent to meet the operating costs.

All these factors coming within months of each other threw the operation of local bus services into turmoil. As far as the public was concerned, however, the only thing they could see was a massive fare increase for the same service. In fact, the public's response was much less hostile than many operators feared. The public knew very well that a cheap-fares policy was heavily subsidised, costing millions of pounds per year, and accepted, usually with resignation, the inevitable.

Our philosophy has therefore changed, but I don't think my management style has. I still think communication is the key factor both up and down the organisation. The new structure has cut out many levels of hierarchy in the organisation and that means that we can get a decision acted upon much more quickly. As I said earlier, I believe in delegation. We have six large and two small garages which are each allocated routes, and the garage itself is responsible for those routes. The staff must schedule the vehicles and crew to meet the frequency requirements of those routes. They must ensure that they keep up a good vehicle-maintenance programme. Obviously we at Head Office monitor what's going on, and not only through our statistics. I am certain that the only way to manage is to go to the place where the work is done. People who work on the routes know the wheezes. They know how to squeeze that extra minute out of a schedule.

Since deregulation, bus drivers see other operators' buses on their routes. They know that competition exists and we are finding that they are becoming increasingly motivated to improve the service they offer. The motivation is less in evidence with the maintenance workers in the garages. I am sure this is because the underneath of a deregulated bus is just the same as that of a regulated bus. The change is not so apparent to them.

We still have to improve productivity. We have too many spare vehicles and too big a workforce. We pay the maintenance workers a flat rate as long as they reach a productivity standard of 75−80 per cent. The drivers also get paid a flat rate, no matter which day of the week they work, as long as they also achieve a productivity standard of 80 per cent. In their case this is simply % wheel hours/% attendance hours. For the engineers it is a bit more complicated. We use a computerised efficiency scheme based on standard times.

The scheduling of bus services is complex. You need to know not only the times taken for a bus to travel between each point on the service routes when loaded, but also the time it takes for buses travelling empty between routes. When empty, buses can cut across the city, off the service routes, so we have to consider low bridges, and 'access-only' roads all over the city to minimise this 'light running' time, because this is costing us money and bringing in no revenue. So we use two matrices: a 'loaded' and a 'light' matrix to record this information. We need yet another matrix to cover things like the time it takes for a driver to walk between the canteen and the bus stations and the time it takes him to sign on and off.

Rostering of bus crews is a major task too. This is carried out differently at different garages. In particular, the degree of union involvement varies. In the past, tentative rosters were produced, and then the union was consulted before the schedules were finally fixed. Agreed schedules are posted for ten days before they come into operation. This enables the crews to plan their family life and activities around their working hours.

Such scheduling problems cried out for computerisation and for the last year we have been introducing a system. It took our schedulers one working month just to put all the data on to the computer. Obviously we have had teething troubles like any other company introducing computerisation, but we are finally winning. However, we need to get more flexibility into the system. A hand scheduler can bend the rules if he is one minute out. A computer can't.

We have had problems. We have had big changes. Our philosophy has had to change. We are learning about marketing our services. We are running a business now, not a public service. This has caused us to try even harder on the operations side, but our operations aim is still the same − to deliver the service specification efficiently.

Operations Manager No. 3 − Production Manager of a Photographic Film Producer

My Company manufactures black-and-white photographic films. We don't try to compete with the big names for the holiday-maker photography market. We focus on niche markets, surveillance, aerial and medical photographs. I am responsible for 700 people on this site.

My job is very varied. Managing the production activities is the more mechanical side of the job. I must look at material costs, the product yields and the waste levels, and see how the actual figures compare with the budget. I need to know what's been going wrong, or, if things are going better than budget, it's just as important to know why that has happened. Any improvements I can make in these areas reflect directly on my operating profit.

I am involved in asset management. I need to take decisions about writing off plant, buying new equipment and getting grants to help us. Obviously I am not involved in day-to-day stock control with such a big set up, but I monitor stocks closely. How can we reduce stocks without reducing the service to customers? That's the secret.

Process efficiency is another one of my concerns. Better material utilisation means you get more product for the same cost, so that's got to be good. An important area of concern in this industry is effluent control. Silver is too expensive to waste and the Water Board don't want it in their water.

People management is probably my major job though. I try to treat people as assets rather than costs. Motivation is essential and means frequent job rotation. I think it helps as well, when you are setting targets, to discuss those targets with the people directly involved. There is some confusion at the moment about who is responsible for what and that's not helpful, but we're putting together a book of job descriptions which should remove some of the grey areas. Still, I don't want things to become too inflexible.

My job is to build a team, so trust is very important. I have got to try to integrate and co-ordinate the different departments. There are 120 managers and supervisors to pull together. One of the things I work hard at is communication. The general level of education of my staff is increasing, so people are no longer just doing as they are told but are asking why. Although this is good, it makes efficient communication even more essential. In such big units it really is difficult to pass a consistent message to everyone in the Company. It can be a bit like Chinese whispers if you're not careful. So every six months I review the communication style, especially the one-to-one communication and the links between my managers. It's important that the employees at every level feel part of the Company. For example, I think a quiet question to a subordinate who has been off sick can serve two positive functions. If an employee has genuinely been off sick, he will be pleased to see that his absence was noticed. If, on the other hand, he has been skiving, then he might be more wary next time.

We are getting more computerised all the time, tempting us managers to stay in our offices, relying on figures from the computer to tell us what's happening in the Works. There is a real danger of losing direct contact with the workforce, so I make positive efforts to walk around and talk to people. After all, people are the hub of the business and you can often learn a lot more if you keep your eyes and ears open and talk to people, than you can from just a set of numbers.

Operations Manager No. 4 – Building Society Branch Manager

Before I start, I had better explain what a building society is about. We used to be simply in the business of helping people buy houses. Now we are also interested in making 'surpluses' (a building society word for profits). My Branch has 61 employees and we now have Branch targets and performance criteria. A branch manager cannot have total control over the performance of his branch. Obviously there are factors both from within the Society and outside which affect performance. For example, national advertising campaigns affect the level of business in an individual branch, but by looking at the types of account featured in the campaign, the accounts of that type opened during the campaign, and the Branch's past performance, we can still work out what improvement is due to Branch operations and what is due to national effort.

We have extended our services considerably since deregulation. For example, we now offer life assurance, traveller's cheques and we have taken over some estate agencies. But really we are only interested in taking on profitable products. We don't want to compete with banks on all their services — that wouldn't make commercial sense — just the profitable areas for us.

I suppose I have two major tasks as branch manager:

(i) the efficient running of the Branch;
(ii) increasing the sales of the Branch.

I aim to satisfy my customers by offering the best service I can, whilst keeping my costs down to an acceptable level so that I can make a reasonable 'surplus'. To do this I have to look at my Branch systems. For example, how can I devise a system to improve the speed with which our Branch can deal with loan applications, and get it down to less than the present average of ten working days? Continually, the system needs checking, improving, monitoring. Customers don't want to wait for weeks to see if we can offer them a mortgage. The customer is king. We must offer this service faster than anyone else. This involves efficient paper work, getting references quickly, getting a valuer into the house to be bought quickly, processing his report quickly, and making a decision quickly. Obviously we get bottlenecks. Now we have our system working so well our bottleneck is usually the vendor, who won't let the valuer come to look for a couple of days! We are looking at taking valuers on to our own staff, rather than employing external people: not because of speed, but because of cost. As long as we have the business to support them, it's cheaper.

I vet all loan applications personally. It's too important an area to risk things going wrong. Usually I rubber-stamp 90 per cent, but the remaining 10 per cent make the difference between Branch success and failure. I check for tell-tale signs of problems. For example, will the person be able to keep up payments? Experience tells us that the most vulnerable clients are probably people employed in sales, who have been in their job for less than one year, working on commission. We build up a picture of bad risks from experience. Also location can lead me to reject applications. Some areas are bedevilled with structural problems, or maybe it's the type of accommodation. Studio apartments are fine in London but in a large housing development on the edge of Sheffield they would be pretty hard to sell.

I suppose these applications take me about 1½ hours each day. I do it first thing each morning. Any problem cases I write up as case studies so that my interviewing staff will begin to gain experience of when to reject applications outright. This should eventually mean less applications come to me that I need to turn down, and more that I can rubber-stamp. It should save me time and I hope will pass on my experience to my staff.

I have also got responsibility for training my staff. As I said, I do it informally with case studies but staff also go on formal courses. My staff must be able to answer customers' queries and not have to wander away from the desk to seek advice. Our image is important and I always stand in the customer queue to carry out my transactions, to see what's going on from the customers' viewpoint. Do I need to improve the presentation of the banking hall? Have I got enough cashiers on? This is a big problem. On the counters, we use a lot of part-timers who only have a quarter of an hour break, otherwise we get real lunch-time problems. Obviously when the situation gets really busy we have to supplement these with full-timers. Scheduling staff is a major problem and we need to plan staff schedules up to six months ahead to take care of holidays and other problems.

I believe in 'managing by walking around' as Peters & Waterman say. You pick up ideas, you know what's happening. I don't try to be good at all my employees' jobs. I need a team each with his or her own skills, although obviously some flexibility is necessary. For example I don't think it is necessary, or even a good idea, for me to learn how to get a balance off the computer. If I ask a young junior to do this, she feels important. She is doing something I can't and she sees that we all have our own job to do.

Basically I see my job as being involved with systems and people: an all-round management job.

Exercise

Contact an operations manager and ask about his or her job, the problems encountered and the skills needed to overcome them. With reference to the operations manager's organisation, try to cover as many of the following points as possible in a half-hour interview.

What product(s) or service(s) does it provide?
Who are its customers?
Who are its main rivals?
What is the history of its development?
How does the operation manager's function fit into the total
    framework of his/her business?
To whom is he/she accountable?
What are his/her main duties?
What is his/her management philosophy?

Further Reading

Full particulars of the standard texts and case-study books can be found in the Bibliography at the end of this book.

Standard Texts

Chase and Aquilano (1981) Chapter 1.
Dilworth (1986) Chapter 1.

Hill (1983) Chapter 1.
Schmenner (1987) Segment 1, Norcen Industries and Thalhimers Cloverleaf Mall
   Store.

Specialist Texts

Harvey-Jones, J. (1988) *Making it Happen,* Collins.
Peters, T.J. and Waterman, R.H. (1982) *In Search of Excellence,* Warner Books,
   New York.
Townsend, R. (1970) *Up the Organisation,* Joseph.
These books explore how good management style can affect all aspects of a
business.

   Apart from books, the most easily accessible and up-to-date descriptions of
operating managers in action can be found in:

Financial Times daily 'management' page
Management Today
Harvard Business Review

Chapter 2

THE PRODUCT

The Product and the Customer

Q. How should a product be defined?

A. There isn't *one* correct definition. A product is a sum of many attributes. This has important consequences for how a product is designed, manufactured, and distributed. For example, take a packaged breakfast cereal, say a sweetened muesli. . . .

Is it:

- a mixture of fruit, cereals, and nuts *(producer's definition)*?
- an instant breakfast *(customer utility)*?
- a path to health and fitness *(customer dream)*?
- a source of income to dentists *(third-party interest)*?

All customers do not seek the same 'benefits' from a product; or at least do not attach the same importance to each benefit. Thus different brands are produced which satisfy different customers' needs.

Consider the reasons why toothpaste might be bought by one particular type of consumer (say a mother of children).

Primary reasons:

(1) It prevents tooth decay.
(2) It clears plaque.

Secondary reasons:

(1) It has an acceptable taste to children.
(2) It can be squeezed properly from the tube.

Now consider the reasons for a different type of consumer (say a teenager) buying toothpaste.

Primary reasons:

(1) It guarantees fresh breath.
(2) It makes teeth appear ultra-bright.

Secondary reasons:

(1) It prevents tooth decay.
(2) It has a low retail price.

The above analyses are the province of market research, which classifies customers according to the different benefits that each class of customer seeks from a product, and quantifies the values put on these benefits. When such information has been found, those in business will know how best to enhance the *intrinsic worth* of their product. This intrinsic worth can be regarded as a rock-bottom, no-frills-added version of the product, very rarely in a form suitable for or appealing to the customer. For example if you are selling perfume, its worth will be enhanced by such things as:

- a famous brand name (e.g. Chanel or St Laurent);
- packaging it in an expensive-looking container with sophisticated colours;
- selling it through highly-regarded outlets such as Harrods;
- selling it at a high price so that the consumer believes he or she is joining an exclusive 'set'.

In marketing terms, this means successful co-ordination of the product, promotion, place and pricing strategies. These broad categories are in practice broken down further; for example, the 'product' strategy would involve such things as delivery and installation assistance, guarantees and insurance cover, and after-sales service.

The Marketing—Production Interface

All the above considerations influence the product-development team when they are considering the following sorts of option open to them:

- product formulae variations (e.g. ingredients in instant soups);
- product shapes (e.g. cylindrical, square or cone-shaped litter bins);
- product packaging (e.g. bottles, cans or paper cartons for soft drinks);
- product styling (e.g. when designing a new car).

These options, whilst providing the customer with added value, incur extra production and distribution costs. However, the business takes up these options voluntarily in the expectation of greater profit. Other variations will be unavoidable. A normal clothes shop is expected to provide a service for all people from children to outsize persons. Their task is made a little easier by the widely known standard sizes for shoes, dresses, shirts and trousers. Nevertheless, the retailer and wholesaler have to hold high stocks of finished goods to enable them to provide a service to the customer with immediate delivery from stock. This has made largely obsolescent the make-to-order system of buying clothes, with a 1–6-week delay in delivery. Note that the older make-to-order system forced the manufacturer/wholesaler to hold high stocks of raw materials such as cloth, and inhibited the adoption of efficient methods of mass production.

Apart from clothing, standardisation is common in many other products – e.g. standard weights for tinned foods and octane ratings for petrol. Not all standardisation originates directly from consumer wishes. The government imposes safety standards for seat belts and electric plugs and health standards for the lead content of petrol. In other circumstances there might be outdated historic reasons for a standard that has only survived through consumer inertia or familiarity. Margarine is dyed to a certain shade of yellow because it is expected to look like butter; it will take many more years of decimalisation before centimetres, litres and kilos totally replace inches, pints and pounds; supertankers deliver oil still measured in 'barrels'; and car (and even aeroplane) engines are still assigned a 'horsepower'.

The Impact of New Technology

New technology is changing the product design and development process. Computer-aided design (CAD) is being used extensively in many types of operation. What is CAD? CAD systems enable you to design a product on a computer-terminal screen. The computer stores the design and then lets you manipulate it. Most CAD systems now show you a three-dimensional image of your design and allow you to look at this image from any angle you like. This gives a much more complete picture of the product than does a representation on a draughtsman's drawing board.

Not only this – if, for example, you were designing an aircraft wing, you can simulate on the screen the effect of vibration or stress at any point. Any changes suggested by the simulation can be incorporated into the design via the CAD screen. You can therefore test and update designs on the computer, without the need for physical models at each stage. This saves both time and money. The Ford Motor Company claim that the average engineer can produce three times as much work in a given period at a CAD workstation than at a draughting table. CAD systems also produce the finished blueprints for manufacture of the physical product. They can generate cutting paths for machining. Software is now available to convert the output from such a system into machine-tool control language and produce a magnetic or paper tape which can then be used directly to control the machine tool.

One such package, DUCT by Deltacam, produces coloured, very detailed representations on a VDU screen. Some idea of their quality can be assessed by looking at the black-and-white reproductions in Figures 2.1, 2.2 and 2.3.

You can see the apparent solidity of the loudspeaker case in Figure 2.1 and make judgements on its aesthetic appeal − even though the product has not yet been produced, even in model form.

But CAD is not just a useful tool for manufacturers. Transport, retail and service organisations can benefit. British Coal's transport systems have been simulated graphically at a computer terminal and their package HAULSTAR is described in Chapter 5. The operation of a Burger Bar can be designed by CAD and interactive simulation techniques. Simulations showing staff and customer movements with different kitchen and counter layouts are carried out to achieve an effective working system. Customer-flow patterns around a retail store can be simulated and, via CAD, the pattern and spacing of aisles adjusted.

All these CAD applications demonstrate how new technology can help in product design and development. Time and money can be saved, but the final test of the product design is always its acceptance by the customer.

Product Development

When a business consultant is approached by a new client, what are the first words that the new client says? In our experience, by far the commonest opening request is: 'I've just developed this marvellous product. All I need now is for you to get me the customers for it.' This is *not* the right way to success. You must have intimate contact with your consumers *before* and *during* product development. The right way to go about development is exemplified by Westall Richardson, a Sheffield cutlery manufacturer who has consistently expanded whilst the UK cutlery industry has drastically declined.

In the early 1980s, out of a workforce of 250, ten people worked full-time on the development of new products. In addition, prototypes were always being passed around the desks of top management for their comments. As customers were always given a hot line to top management, there was a bridge between customers and developers. At that time, Westall Richardson noticed that customers expressed interest in obtaining knives that never needed sharpening. Whilst developing such a knife they carried

Figure 2.1 Loudspeaker case — finished prototype

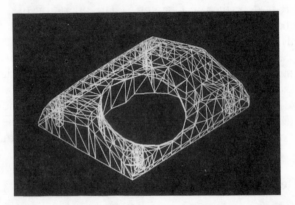

Figure 2.2 Loudspeaker case — finite element mesh

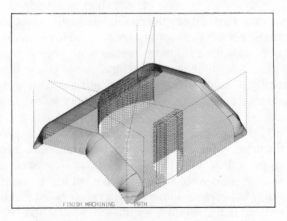

FINISH MACHINING   PATH

Figure 2.3 Loudspeaker case — cutter path

out fundamental research on optimum cutting angles. These researches indicated that the cutting edge could be increased by 50 per cent by using a waved configuration along the sharp side of the knife. Any customer resistance to such an unusual shape was overcome by the 25-year guarantee that came with the knife. By such a combination of: (a) desirable characteristics in the product, and (b) attention to the consumer, Westall Richardson has emerged as the largest producer of knife blades in Europe.

Value Analysis

In the public mind, new products are thought to spring into life after an inventor has a sudden brainwave. In fact nearly all innovation is a long, hard grind of little improvements and modifications grafted on to existing products. This process has been formalised under a technique known as *Value Analysis*.

Classic Principles of Value Analysis

Value Analysis is a method of taking a fresh look at the design of an existing product. Its origins go back to the Second World War. During that period H.L. Erlicher, Purchasing Officer for General Electric Company (USA) observed that:

- a shortage of non-ferrous metals forced designers and production planners to search for temporary substitute materials;
- when things returned to normal, people were surprised to find that the supposed 'second-best substitutes' were cheaper and of better quality then the original material *and had been all along*.

These observations inspired another GEC employee, L.D. Miles, to see if the resourcefulness evident in wartime could be maintained during peacetime. From 1947 to 1951 Miles headed a Value Analysis section of GEC. Its success led to the adoption of Value Analysis by GEC's suppliers, customers and competitors. The US Department of Defense was so impressed by the improvements achieved by Value Analysis companies that it became a strongly recommended business technique for defence suppliers.

Below are some major features of early value analysis.

(1) Moving towards the consumer's viewpoint   Value Analysis was an early attempt to give product development some customer orientation. It introduced the concepts of 'use' and 'esteem' as separate functions of the product. On the other hand, Value Analysis has often been incorrectly

pigeon-holed as a 'cost-reduction exercise'. This cannot be right. If customers don't want your product you are not going to rescue the situation by reducing costs.

(2) Listing and classifying   Miles took great care in defining exhaustive lists and classifications of components, processes and ways of doing things. This was to ensure that no alternative was overlooked.

(3) Snappy assessment of functions and generation of alternatives   This states, in simple English, what every component contributes to the final product. Preferably this is done in two words, though we feel there is no need to make a fetish of this. Also, it should record the *primary* rather than the *secondary* function. Thus paint prolongs the life of a car rather than looks good. Other examples from a car could be:

> *headrest* − ameliorates whiplash injury
> *choke* − helps cold-starts
> *jack* − enables DIY wheel-change
> *car-stereo* − entertains driver

Next a full list of alternatives is sought for every part. Here, the value of the snappy functions becomes apparent: if you focus on them, it is easier to think of sometimes quite revolutionary alternatives. No alternative should be excluded, and every alternative should have a rough estimate of cost and other major characteristics attached. After an elementary cost or break-even analysis, a choice between alternatives is made.

(4) Removing the roadblocks to creativity   Everyone desires a certain level of stability in their lives. But it is easy for this to degenerate into the 'locked-in' behaviour of tradition and ritual. In such circumstances new ideas can be actively suppressed. Value analysts try to identify road-blocks to a solution both in their own and their colleagues' behaviour. These road-blocks may be:

> *(a)*   *Perceptual*   For example, rejecting a worthwhile invention that 'defies commonsense'. To understand why aircraft can fly requires the mind to leap to an understanding of wing configuration, airspeed and pressure differences.
>
> *(b)*   *Emotional*   For example, the tendency, a few years ago, for the West to dismiss Japan's economic resurgence because they were stereotyped as imitators and producers of shoddy goods.
>
> *(c)*   *Habitual*   Resistance is often strongest from a skilled operator of an existing method; for example, a professional pianist would not be too enthusiastic about music synthesisers. Companies with long experience in a product area become

set in their ideas; for example, the game Monopoly was rejected by several games producers because it took longer to play the game than other successful products. This was assumed to be unacceptable to consumers.

(d)   *Cultural* Human social groups, religions, nations or professions are extremely stubborn when suggestions are made to 'improve' their supposedly inefficient practices. They need these practices to preserve their identity.

(e)   *Embarrassment* The originator of Value Analysis, L.D. Miles, greatly stressed this feature, though subsequent exponents have rather ignored it. Miles thought that value analysts didn't like to appear foolish when approaching experts. Also many value analysts fear rebuffs and this inhibits them from contacting strangers to ask for a favour. And finally experts themselves feel embarrassed if they are put in a probing situation where their own ignorance might be revealed.

(5) Implementation   Obtaining a new component often involves a crucial decision: *How*? In its broadest context this can be summarised as in Figure 2.4. This shows the general trade-off that has to be made between speed of adoption and cost. If speedy alternatives are chosen (like importing ready-made or part-assembly), great responsibility is vested in the purchasing and materials manager. If long-run, low-operating-cost alternatives are chosen (such as subcontracting or self-manufacture), there is greater responsibility vested in the works manager or industrial engineer.

Figure 2.4

Recent Developments in the Value Analysis Area

(1) Moving towards the consumer's viewpoint The greater impact of marketing on business operations has led to scientific analysis of what the

consumer looks for in a product. This approach was discussed briefly in the introduction to this chapter.

(2) Listing and classifying   Originally this could be regarded as an exercise *internal* to the organisation (e.g. checking on tolerances, waste, standardisation of parts, stocking and manufacturing procedures). Now there are moves to make more exhaustive, *external* investigations (e.g. listing and classifying all suppliers and contacts, and finding out what your rivals are up to).

(3) Snappy assessment of functions and generation of alternatives   It may be a retrograde step, but there are moves to more complicated *global* rather than bit-by-bit assessments. These are implicit in capital-budgeting techniques for the whole project and in multiple-criterion decision making.

(4) Roadblocks to creativity   Originally Value Analysis was run by company departments of internal experts. When it became a vogue technique in the 1950s it became a standard service of certain management consultants. In the 1960s and 1970s it rather fell out of fashion. In the 1980s there has been a renewed interest in Value Analysis partly because many of its features appear in the management of Quality Circles. In particular, attention is focusing on how to stimulate shopfloor creativity.

(5) Implementation   There has been greater experimentation with team-work inside and outside the organisation. In Japan, innovation has accelerated because big organisations delegate the control of development to prime subcontractors. These in their turn control development work in companies to whom they subcontract work, typically consisting of fewer than ten workers, usually young graduates willing to work ridiculously long hours to achieve success. The same attitude can be observed in small software-development teams all over the world, but only the Japanese seem to have extended it to wider operations-management applications.

CASE STUDY: VALUE ANALYSIS DURING PRODUCT DEVELOPMENT

Warlord is a board game for 2–6 players. The players are generals and take it in turn to move and attack each other with 'bombs' and 'armies'. A die is used, not as a random element but as a medium for out-thinking the enemy. As the game progresses more of the board becomes 'radioactive' and out of bounds to players' armies. Eventually only one player's armies are left and he or she wins. For 6 years Warlord was sold on

demand in small quantities (under 100 sets a year) by its
designer. In 1977 a wholesaler, Games Workshop, began to
distribute it and demand started to rise. Larger batches had to
be made to accommodate this demand, causing all sorts of
organisational problems to the designer, who made up games
in the attic of his house. In January 1979, Games Workshop
came back to the inventor and said it was unhappy that such
small batches were being made. If it was going to continue
marketing the game, it wanted a supply of at least 500 sets during
1979 and probably many more for 1980 onwards. The following
notes were made by the inventor when he reviewed the situation
before making the larger batch for 1979.

Exercise

1. From the information available, what market is this game
   aimed at? What do you assess to be the primary and
   secondary reasons for the main class of consumers buying
   this sort of product?
2. In this case the list of components is readily available. For
   each component can you make a snappy assessment of its
   function and generate alternatives?
3. As you read through this case you will have noticed certain
   road-blocks holding up the inventor's progress. What are
   they?
4. In brief, what would you have done to meet demand in 1979?

*Estimated Costs as at 1 January 1979, based on the
Existing Mode of Operation*

(1) Sunk costs These costs had already been incurred and
would not be incurred again if a new batch of the same product
were assembled:

Drawing materials	£40
Artwork and design	£410
Litho plates of maps	£430
Typesetting of rules	£120

(2) Set-up costs These were applicable for each new batch
made, regardless of batch size:

Material procurement and delivery	£80
Litho machine set-up costs	£170

(3) Variable material costs

	For the boxed set (£ per game)	For a 'polyfolio' half-set (£ per game)
Outer boxes	0.24	0.20 (for the polyfolio casing)
Box labels	0.10	—
Maps on boards	0.80	0.20
Rules	0.15	0.15
Dice	0.10	0.10
Counters material	0.25	0.10
Counters guillotining	0.35	0.16
Lego units	0.30	0.15
Plastic bags	0.06	0.06

Semi-variable 'intangible' costs

	For the boxed set (£ per game)	For a 'polyfolio' half-set (£ per game)
Assembly	0.15	0.05
Delivery	1.05	0.65
Accounts	0.10	0.05
Interest on stock	0.10	0.04

A Note on the Reliability of the (then) Existing Suppliers (all costs quoted are at January 1979 prices)

The printer who supplied the maps and rules had a first-class reputation for quality but his prices, though competitive, were not cheap. Also he was working very near to full capacity and at some times of the year needed 6 weeks' notice to complete maps. On top of this, the printer had to arrange for a sub-contractor to stick the maps to boards and get them guillotined. There were not many firms who had the facilities to stick and cut boards of this size. The last time the printer made a batch, he had to go to a West London firm, which took 3 weeks to do the job. The outer boxes were made by Remploy. They were remarkably cheap and offered prices which were 30−50p below those offered by other Sheffield box-makers for a similar product. They also offered a quick service − e.g. an order placed on 20 December was delivered on 30 December! However they did not stock a large range of board material. Anything of a special colour or thickness had to be provided by the customer. Cardboard could be purchased for this purpose from any one of several mills in the Macclesfield area. By shopping around, imperfect board could be obtained at 33 – 50 per cent discount of the current material cost. Board was also bought from these mills to be cut up into counters. There were several reasons why this was not an ideal practice:

(1) It was difficult to get boards of sufficient thickness in the full range of colours necessary to make counters.

(2) Usually the boards were only coloured on one side. It would look much better if they were coloured on both sides. It would be best to buy a thick plain board and have it silk-screened in the required colours.

(3) It was difficult to cut up the board into counters. Sometimes the colouring flaked, sometimes the counters came out in the wrong size or shape. The pre-1979 arrangement was for a small printing firm to cut up the board into counters. The boards were stacked 25 deep and cut into ½-inch strips by a 32-inch capacity Adana guillotine. The strips were then taped together at various points and cut crossways, giving ½-inch square counters. The process required a considerable amount of skill and took up a lot of the operator's time. It took him a whole day to cut enough counters for 100 games. Increasingly, the firm was finding it difficult to fit in this job with the other work it had to do. In January 1979 they could not promise delivery within two months. When other firms were given sample boards to cut up (with a view to placing a large order with them) they did not have the skill to match the result of the existing firm.

Some alternative way of obtaining counters had to be found quickly (this was an urgent problem as stocks of existing counters had nearly run out). One possibility was to use plastic tiddleywink counters. These could be obtained from Martins importers for £1.60 per set. They were made in Hong Kong and were cheaper than any British product. Enquiries were made for the British manufacture of these items but the initial quotations were discouraging. It would cost £960 to pay for the moulds (with a 3-month lead time) and the variable cost would be approximately £1.40 per set. Enquiries to eight local plastics firms asking if they already possessed moulds which would be suitable produced a negative response. Another possibility was to investigate the use of another raw material for counters, such as tile or rubber, clay or tin. In terms of consumer preference, one is looking for a counter that keeps its shape, with a colour that stands out, which won't slide about on the boards, and that looks clean. Obtaining counters was the most knotty problem to solve. The remaining items (bags, dice, polyfolios and labels) were easy to obtain from several sources.

Issues which Crossed the Inventor's Mind as He Wondered what to Do Next

- What favourable characteristics and strong points were possessed by games similar to Warlord which were currently available from the shops?
- Could Warlord match or excel these characteristics?
- What distribution outlets were being used by competing products?
- Were there any outlets which had been overlooked or were under-exploited?
- What types of outlet should Warlord seek to exploit, initially and long-term?
- How much resources should be devoted to a promotional campaign?
- If there was to be some kind of promotion, should it be in the form of adverts, brochures or trade stands? And at whom should these be directed?
- How important was the impact of the packaging on the consumer?
- How much money was it reasonable to devote to the packaging?
- Does the evidence suggest that some games (e.g. Dungeons and Dragons) sold well because of the exceptionally high quality of the artwork on their cover? If so, should Warlord follow suit?

Atomistic Analysis

This asked very detailed questions about each component. We have already discussed the counters. These questions were asked about the box:

- What is the ideal size (length, height and width) from the point of view of the consumer, the retailer, for delivery or postage, or for storage?

- Likewise, what was the ideal weight?
- What material should the game be encased in? Wood? Cardboard? Paper? Heavy inflexible plastic? Polystyrene? Light flexible transparent plastic?
- How should the materials be held together? Screwed or glued (for wood)? Gummed, stitched or slitted (for cardboard)? Moulded or pressed (for plastics)?
- What opening method should be adopted? An inner and outer box? A hinge? A bookcase file? A slit or zip?
- How robust should the cover be? Should it be impervious to stain and water? How much strain should it be able to stand when being assembled; stored; delivered; used by the consumer?
- What internal structure should the box possess? Should the equipment be packed loosely or in any particular order? Should trays, boxes or compartments be provided?
- What display characteristics should the box possess? How pleasing should the artwork be? What words, motifs, marks or logos should appear? Should any particular attention be given to the sides or back of the box?

Questions Going Beyond Value Analysis

What systems of cash management should be adopted? Should one delay payment to suppliers or ask for a discount for immediate cash payment? Likewise should customers be asked to pay cash on the nail, or within a fixed period, or should discounts be offered for prompt payment? Should discounts be offered to customers who place bulk orders? What size should those discounts be? When should decisions be taken which have long-term fundamental effects on the course of the project? What are the leading indicators which assess the progress of the project? What circumstances would indicate that the project should be abandoned? Should the project be passed on or sold to someone else? Was it worth considering a partnership or joint enterprise? What circumstances would indicate that it is worth making a major modification in design? What circumstances indicate that expansion is necessary? How should this be financed?

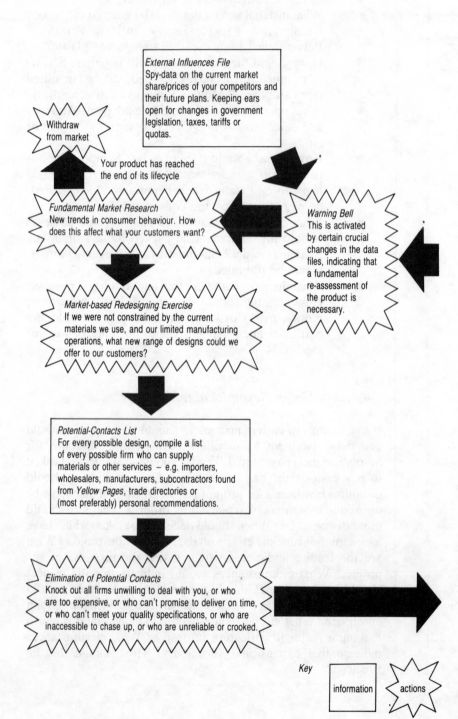

External Influences File
Spy-data on the current market
share/prices of your competitors and
their future plans. Keeping ears
open for changes in government
legislation, taxes, tariffs or
quotas.

Withdraw
from market

Your product has reached
the end of its lifecycle

Fundamental Market Research
New trends in consumer behaviour. How
does this affect what your customers want?

Warning Bell
This is activated
by certain crucial
changes in the data
files, indicating that
a fundamental
re-assessment of
the product is
necessary.

Market-based Redesigning Exercise
If we were not constrained by the current
materials we use, and our limited manufacturing
operations, what new range of designs could we
offer to our customers?

Potential-Contacts List
For every possible design, compile a list
of every possible firm who can supply
materials or other services – e.g. importers,
wholesalers, manufacturers, subcontractors found
from Yellow Pages, trade directories or
(most preferably) personal recommendations.

Elimination of Potential Contacts
Knock out all firms unwilling to deal with you, or who
are too expensive, or who can't promise to deliver on time,
or who can't meet your quality specifications, or who are
inaccessible to chase up, or who are unreliable or crooked.

Key

information   actions

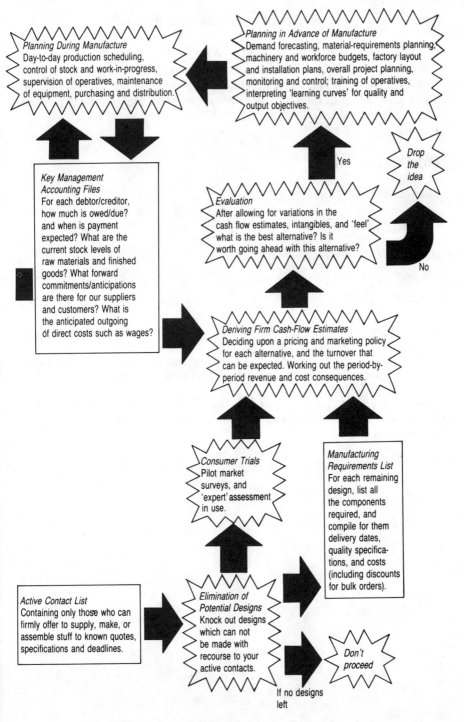

Figure 2.5 The product development and assessment cycle

The Product Development and Assessment Cycle

The questions asked at the end of the Warlord case study show that there is no clear break between Value Analysis and matters that affect the total viability of a business. Matters relating to product development must be put in the context of total business operations. This can best be expressed in the diagram shown in Figure 2.5.

Further Reading

Standard Texts

Delmar (1985) Chapter 2.
Evans *et al.* (1987) Chapter 4.
Hunter (1983) Chapter 7.

Specialist Texts

Gruenwald, G. (1985) *New Product Development,* NTC Business Books. Easy to read, informative, US hardback.
Jewkes, J. *et al.* (1969) *The Sources of Invention,* 2nd edn, Måcmillan. Fascinating set of cases and comments on twentieth-century inventions and what got them off the ground.
Miles, L.D. (1961) *Techniques of Value Analysis and Engineering,* McGraw-Hill. Persuasive, informative book by Value Analysis's founder.

Case Studies

Nicholson (1978) Micronair.

Chapter 3

MACHINES

Introduction

What is a machine?

A machine is more than a tool (a spanner) or a container (a silo) or a monitor (a gas meter). But it is less than an industrial plant (a nuclear power station) or a workshop (a car-repair workshop) or a distribution system (a telephone network).

A machine rarely needs more than a few human operators. Typically, it takes in power and manipulates something. And it is usually superior to an unaided human in at least one of these respects: **speed, strength, accuracy, cost**.

Typically a machine converts inputs into outputs.

Classification of inputs:

Labour − operating, maintenance and supervision
Materials − at many stages from raw (iron ore) to finished (iron screw)
Power and utilities − electricity, gases, coal, oil, steam, water, air
Capital items − permanent casings, replaceable mechanisms, control equipment
Support equipment − e.g. fans, tools and loaders

Classification of outputs:

Products and materials − embracing semi-finished to consumer products, including by-products
Power and utilities − where the machine is a power provider (see the input classification above)

Services and indirect benefits – monitoring, transportation, medical and entertainment functions

Pollutants – e.g. noise, effluent, heat, dust, smoke, poisons and other health hazards

Recommended First Approach to Understanding a Machine

(1) Initially, ignore the internal workings of a machine.
(2) Identify all the inputs and outputs.
(3) Identify where all the inputs come from and where all the outputs go to.
(4) Summarise your information in a diagram.

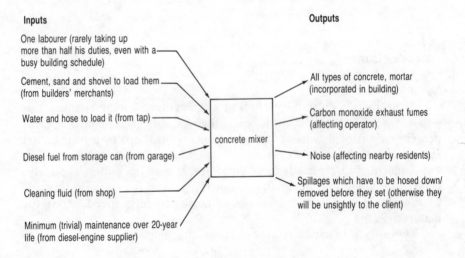

Inputs

One labourer (rarely taking up more than half his duties, even with a busy building schedule)

Cement, sand and shovel to load them (from builders' merchants)

Water and hose to load it (from tap)

Diesel fuel from storage can (from garage)

Cleaning fluid (from shop)

Minimum (trivial) maintenance over 20-year life (from diesel-engine supplier)

concrete mixer

Outputs

All types of concrete, mortar (incorporated in building)

Carbon monoxide exhaust fumes (affecting operator)

Noise (affecting nearby residents)

Spillages which have to be hosed down/removed before they set (otherwise they will be unsightly to the client)

Figure 3.1 The basic inputs and outputs of a concrete mixer

| **Classroom Exercise** | *(5 minutes)* |

1. Choose one of the following: a typewriter, a drinks-dispensing machine or a washing machine.
2. Draw all the inputs into and the outputs from that machine.
3. Say where every input has come from, and where every output is going to.

Throughput

Introduction

So far we have treated the machine as a *'black box'*. Inputs enter and, after some mysterious *transformation*, outputs emerge. What types of transformation could be involved? Here are some examples: breaking up (cement-plant), binding (brick-plant), mixing (bread), cutting (lawn-mowing), reshaping (drop forging), transporting (vehicles), power generation (turbine) or chemical conversion (polyethylene production). In most of these cases you find the method of measuring inputs is different from that of measuring outputs.

Should inputs or outputs be used as the true measure of the machine's efficiency? Is there some internal measure that can be used? This is often a tricky problem. In particular beware of the term *capacity*, which indicates a theoretical maximum at one point of time. *Throughput* is a far more relevant economic concept; it defines a volume which can be feasibly held over a period of time.

Example: A Japanese−English Translating Machine

Equipment　One computer with a special keyboard, one VDU, a printer and a hard disk unit.

The transformation process　A sentence is typed into the machine via the computer keyboard. Both kana (phonetic script) and kanji (Chinese-type characters) are accepted. The text of what has been typed in then appears on the screen and may be amended before processing. When the text is sent to be translated, a dictionary data bank looks up all alternative meanings for every word. Within a sentence, every combination of alternative words is tested and a scoring system rejects the weakest links. The strongest combinations are then converted from a Japanese to an English sentence pattern, with special adjustment for plurals and the tense of verbs. All possible translations from the original Japanese sentence are then displayed in English on a screen. An interactive system allows the operator to edit the result.

Throughput　The speed and potential for processing is severely handicapped by the space taken up by the dictionary: only half of the hard disk's 40 megabytes is available to the user. The interactive nature of the machine means that speed and quality are very sensitive to the skill of the operator. Heavy demands on it meant that it was working 24 hours a day employing three operators, each on an 8-hour shift. The main delay arises from errors in programming and from shortcomings in the operating system. Secondly, the printer to which output is sent frequently breaks down. Every time the system has to start up after a breakdown there is a 10-minute delay whilst the components co-ordinate (bootstrap) themselves.

Reasons Why a Machine Might Not Reach Maximum Throughput

(1) To comply with safety regulations   e.g. to avoid a machine overheating, or to avoid excessive vibrations which might cause an accident, or to avoid danger to the operative.

(2) During warm-up and run-down periods   e.g. the acceleration and deceleration period of a train. Certain chemical processors (e.g. a catalytic cracking plant) may take a day or so starting from cold before they are ticking over and handling maximum volume. Likewise nuclear reactors cannot be suddenly halted but must pass through a protracted closing-down process.

(3) Resetting a machine to make a different product   For example, in injection moulding it might take several hours to remove one mould from a machine and install a new mould, together with jigs and support apparatus.

(4) Removing a product from the machine   This applies to dangerous or delicate products, or where many jigs and fixtures to the product have to be removed (e.g. removing a patient after a surgical or dental operation).

(5) When a machine is slowed or stopped to replenish material   e.g. when a printer or photocopier has to be reloaded with paper although a print run has not been completed.

(6) To carry out a routine inspection and possible replacement of parts   e.g. a car undergoing its MOT test.

(7) Accidents and unexpected breakdowns   Notice that with aeroplanes this applies not only to the immediate loss of any plane that crashes but to the possible grounding of all similar machines while safety checks are made.

(8) A shortage of inputs   e.g. difficulty in recruiting operatives for evening and night shifts and shortage caused by stockpiling and speculation in precious metals.

(9) Potential output in excess of demand   For example, the spread of

narrow-strip razor blades has made uneconomic many of the rolling mills making the special steel strip for this purpose.

(10) Changing environmental constraints e.g. the weather's effect on the performance of harvesting machines.

(11) System interruptions affecting the machine If a machine is part of a complex system of machines then the throughput of another machine might be affected by reasons 1 – 10. For instance, all sorts of machines in a steel plant might suffer from the malfunctioning of an overhead crane.

Example: Throughput Losses on an Offset-litho Printing Machine

(1) Daily start-up and run-down time At the beginning of the day the operator spends 15 minutes preparing ink and sorting out a priority of work. At the end of the day there is a 15-minute cleaning and de-inking period.

(2) Resetting a machine to start a new print run It takes 45 seconds to fit a new batch of stencils.

(3) Operator unavailable because of having to work on a support machine A stencil has to be made for every page of all work submitted. Each stencil takes 15 seconds to make.

(4) Removing a product from the machine It takes 30 seconds to remove work, attach a label to it and place it on shelves for collection.

(5) Replenishing material It takes 40 seconds to load the machine with blank paper. The machine can be loaded whilst it is operating if it is slowed down.

(6) Routine inspection and maintenance The operator disassembles and cleans the machine for her final hour on Friday afternoon. Often, there isn't a backlog of work to be printed at this time. For one morning every month the machine is closed down for a service engineer to go over it.

(7) Accidents and unexpected breakdowns Once (in five years) the machine caught fire due to an electrical short circuit. Twice it has broken down because there was a temporary stand-in who ran the machine at the wrong speed. About twice a month there are hold-ups because poor-quality paper is not passing properly through the machine. This causes a 5-minute delay.

Figure 3.2 An offset-litho printing machine

(8) A shortage of inputs The operator has a higher-than-average absence rate partly because of the noise and stress of the job. There is no real replacement at hand.

(9) Surplus output Almost daily at busy times of the year the operator runs out of shelf space to put finished work. There is a delay as she contacts people to get some of it cleared.

(10) Systems interruptions Occasionally (about once a month) a piece of work gets lost (usually by someone other than the operator). But the operator has to make a big search through past job tickets to see if it has reached her. At busy times, people interrupt the operator trying to get her to give priority to their work.

Classroom Exercise *(10 minutes)*
1. Choose one of the following: a train, a bus, a fish-and-chip frier, a cash-till or a lawnmower
2. How does it convert its inputs to outputs?
3. What could stop you getting maximum throughput?

The Impact of New Technology on Machine Operations

Previously, machine improvements were restricted to mechanisation. Now they are associated with information processing. For example, automatic identification systems are revolutionising the retail trade. Bar codes are now put on to almost all grocery packages. An automatic scanner reads the bar code which identifies the product and the price, and this information is transmitted to an electronic till which automatically adds up the grocery bill as the goods are passed over the scanner. This reduces delays at checkouts. Cashiers no longer have to find out prices for products which haven't been manually price labelled. There are other advantages. Customers receive an itemised bill with product-names as well as prices, making checking easier. More importantly, stores can reduce staff levels since goods do not need stick-on labels before going on the shelves, and price changes can be made at the push of one button.

Advances in computer software along with improvements in manufacturing equipment have led to the development of automatically-controlled machines. Early, numerically controlled (N/C) machines were controlled by instructions fed into the machines on paper tape. Instructions to move, drill and cut were coded and the machine tool automatically performed the required operation communicated to it via the paper tape. Information to change tools, such as drill-bit sizes, were also coded in this way. Now technology has advanced further and microcomputers can control machines. These machines are known as CNC (computer numerical control) machines. Automatic control means that one operator can tend several machines simultaneously. This has radically changed whole manufacturing systems.

Beyond CNC we are now witnessing a further stage in automation. This is the installation of industrial robots. Industrial robots have two main components:

(i)   a manipulator − like a human arm − to perform work;
(ii)   a control system to provide instructions to the manipulator.

Two such robots working on the Austin Rover 800 series assembly line are shown in Figures 3.3 and 3.4.

A robot can be taught to perform sequences of motions and even to make logical decisions. For example, a robot with a scanner can be taught to look at a component and, on the basis of whether it finds a flaw in, for example, a weld, decide whether to accept or reject the component. The manipulator on the robot can then put the 'accepts' into one pile and the 'rejects' into another. (See Chapter 6 for an evaluation of such behaviour.)

Figure 3.3   Robot welding of door assembly

Figure 3.4 Windscreen fitment by robot

The Economic Evaluation of a Machine

Introduction to the Evaluation Analysis

Why do you need to know what a machine earns?

(i)   because it might be losing you money;
(ii)   because you might be considering purchasing a machine and you need to explore alternatives.

Figures given to you by others, even by experts, can be misleading. A salesman selling you a machine might quote you performance figures which can be achieved only under artificially ideal conditions (e.g. when quoting to you the miles per gallon of a car or the response time of a computer software system).

An operator, asked to provide estimates of his or her machine's performance to management is tempted to make them a little pessimistic. Not so pessimistic that the machine's worth (and possibly the operator's job) is questioned, but pessimistic enough for the operator to be able to earn a bonus if management set a standard target to reach based on this estimate.

Depreciation may spread the original capital cost of a machine over a number of years unconnected with the machine's actual life and usage.

From the financial accountant's point of view this might be the most logical way to minimise tax payments.

More frequently a management accountant may allocate all factory expenses between machines in a pretty arbitrary fashion. This is well illustrated in the following example. The written analysis hints at some interesting valuation problems, but these are obscured by the table of allocated costs (Table 3.1) which should not be used to make any decision about the machine, be it an operating or replacement decision.

Example: Analysis of a Clingfilm Winder

The machine produces rolls of clingfilm in four different lengths: 5m, 14m, 30m and 60m. The numbers of rolls the machine can produce per hour for each length are 640, 480, 330 and 200 respectively. Down time is caused by the operator changing the parent roll and resetting for length, by electrical or mechanical failure, by lack of materials or by lack of operators. This does not normally affect output as there are three other machines and two shifts of operators who will keep the machines running from 8 a.m. to 9.30 p.m. if necessary, to meet the company's forecasted demand.

Inputs necessary to keep the machine working, apart from an operator, are film tubes, cartons, shrink film, cases, labels and pallets. Miscellaneous items are sellotape and glue. The machine runs on electricity and compressed air. Some waste is produced which is taken into account when the company prices the product.

The policy of the company is to allocate *manufacturing costs* according to the proportion of total factory machine hours that each machine runs, as shown in Table 3.1.

Table 3.1 Annual manufacturing cost allocated to the clingfilm winder (£s)

Direct wages	22,800
Management salaries	6,500
Maintenance wages	8,800
Repairs and renewals	4,800
Property repairs	1,000
Heating	4,800
Light and power	3,700
Rates, insurance, machine hire	3,600
Depreciation	2,300

These annual allocated costs total £58,300. Dividing this total by the 9,000 hours p.a. that the machine runs, gives a *running cost* of £6.48 per hour. This running cost is then one of several elements used to work out how a product should be priced. They are (running costs per hour × number of hours run) + (cost of material inputs including 3% that goes to waste) + (head office and sales *overheads*) + 5% profit margin. Thus we have a rule-of-thumb method to help determine a cost-plus pricing policy. But this method is not particularly accurate in telling us about a machine's efficiency. This should be done via the more detailed analysis that we are going to explain next.

Costs

You can make correct decisions about a machine only if you know how costs vary with throughput. In particular, operating labour, raw materials, utilities and repair costs are often assumed to be *proportional costs*.

Variable labour costs   Is it easy to match the expense of operating labour with throughput? Take an example. In the manufacture of cutlery there are machines which are fed with 'blanks' (half-finished items) by an operative. He reaches into a tub of blanks by his side, picks one out, inserts it into the machine, positions it correctly and then presses a treadle with his foot. The machine then automatically processes and ejects the blank. This cycle of operations takes 3−5 seconds depending on how easy it is to reach into the tub and how skilled the operator is at positioning the blank correctly. If a straight piece-rate was paid, for example about £1 per 400 blanks, operating labour would be an easy variable cost to calculate. However, even in this simple situation it is quite rare to be paid a sole piece-rate without also being given an attendance allowance, an allowance for unavoidable machine or system down time and a share of a group bonus. Also, such items as national insurance contributions are a cost attributable to operating labour.

For more complex machines, operating labour's relationship to throughput is correspondingly more difficult to define. The volume of throughput might be affected by the varying skill needed to make different products on the same machine. In such circumstances there might be a different rate fixed for each job. In other circumstances the operative might be paid by the hour, or paid overtime, making the connection between throughput and labour cost more difficult to unravel.

Variable material costs   Surely the cost of materials and throughput are connected? For example, surely it is reasonable to assume that, if you are working at (say) 70 per cent of a previous throughput, you will incur 70 per cent of the previous material cost? This simple (and seemingly obvious) proportion rule is surprisingly difficult to verify for the following reasons:

(1) Some material prices change quickly, e.g. within three months the international price of copper or tin might double or halve.

(2) Some machines process materials of significantly different values at different times, e.g. a woodworker's lathe may use rare hardwoods or cheap softwoods, or an electricity-generating station may switch from coal to oil and back again).

(3) Sometimes the input of materials into a machine is impossible to record (e.g. coal into a coal-cutter), can be only approximately measured (e.g. the metering of a pipeline liquid), or is only measured when it is added to a stockpile fronting a machine (e.g. sand unloaded on to a building site is not measured when inputted into mixers).

Variable utility costs   Is there a simple relationship between utility costs and a machine's throughput? For example, if you know the number of hours per year that a conveyor belt has run, is there a simple multiplying factor to tell you the conveyor belt's electricity cost? It is not that easy. There might be an easy formula to tell you the units of electricity (kWh) that have been consumed. But to transfer units consumed to costs, you have to allow for peak-demand surcharges, night-time or bulk-purchase discounts and increased costs if standby generation has had to be used.

Variable repair and maintenance costs   Direct repair and maintenance costs increase with age and usage. Indirectly, there is a hidden cost of lost revenue when a machine is frequently out of service. Also, for older machines there are:

(i)   the delays caused by spare parts being unavailable;
(ii)   the inability to meet the highest quality specifications.

Fixed costs   These costs are insensitive to changes in a machine's throughput. If they have occurred in the past and are not going to recur again they are *sunk costs* and we can ignore them. The remaining fixed costs fall within these classifications:

(1) Some costs are fixed for each order received, regardless of how many items are requested by the order. For example, there is a *set-up cost* involving skilled labour and special materials to make a printing plate, a plastics mould or a clothing pattern.

(2) Some *annual fixed costs* are independent of either the number of orders to be processed or the throughput. For example, the annual licence fee of a vehicle fits into this category. Some fixed costs are included in the general overheads of a firm even though they could be precisely assigned to a machine. For example, an insurance cover note often specifies the premium for each item of equipment. Rent cannot be allocated quite so precisely, but space taken up by the machine is often a reasonable guide. Sometimes crowded offices

retain obsolescent machines (e.g. old computers) for occasional use. Because they have been 'fully depreciated', some managers regard retaining them as involving no cost. This is wrong if the office space could be used for something else.

(3) Extra fixed costs which need to be examined when considering the replacement of a machine. These include:

    (i)   the current purchase price of the new machine – the previous purchase price may be irrelevant because of inflation, obsolescence, technical progress, trade wars by the equipment suppliers or foreign-exchange movements if it is purchased from abroad;

    (ii)   the trade-in or scrap value of your existing machine, including the value of parts which you cannibalise for use on other machines in your organisation (this is an important factor for recovered space satellites);

    (iii) installation costs for the new machine;

    (iv) commissioning costs, teething troubles and the running-in expense whilst bringing a product up to the required standard;

    (v)   demolition and removal charges on the old machine (including the disruption to production and delays in the service to your customers that may result);

    (vi) subsidies and tax allowance including both immediate and future allowable claims.

Indirect costs The two main types of indirect cost are passed-on costs and intangible costs:

(1) *Passed-on costs* are those cost increases (or savings) in other parts of the system which arise when a new machine is introduced into an organisation. For example, a new word processor might not only make a typewriter redundant, it might also replace printing and typesetting machines, and filing cabinets.

    Conversely some new machines which save operating labour may require more machinery elsewhere in the system. Consider a bank's introduction of an advanced on-line computing system which instantly handles money transfers between accounts. This can eliminate some of the paperwork and labour associated with the old cheque-clearing system. But the new system must guard against machine errors, electricity failures and sophisticated frauds. Some banks have got round this problem by installing a parallel system which duplicates the work of the first and, just to be safe, using a different computer manufacturer's hardware, a different source of electricity and a completely independent team of programmers.

Finally, a new, 'more efficient' machine might require higher stock levels to service it, or might be unable to work at a low level of capacity. Compare, for example, nuclear power stations (which can supply only base-load electricity) with gas turbine generators (which can provide the more valuable electricity during peak demand).

(2) *Intangible costs* include costs which, though not easily measured in monetary terms, involve a significant social cost. For example:

    pollution − smoke, river waste, tips
    accidents − from traffic or dangerous cutting machines
    long-term health costs − e.g. affecting X-ray-machine operators,
        garage mechanics, miners, brewery workers and tar sprayers.

Example of Machine Evaluation: Yearly Costs of a Photocopier

Fixed costs (p.a.)
  Fixed service charge = £20

Variable costs (p.a.)

			£
Leasing cost	1.3p/copy	× 180,000 copies	= 2,340
Labour cost	£2.2/hour	× 450 hours	= 990
Paper cost	£3.4/1000	× 180,000	= 612
Ink cost	£3.5/carton	× 40 cartons	= 140
Electricity	6p/kWh × 1.6 kW	× 450 hours	= 44
			4,126

Expanded explanation of these costs   Above 180,000 copies p.a. the leasing cost dropped to 0.9p/copy. By coincidence this machine's actual throughput was exactly at the breakpoint.

    Knowledge of the number of copies produced per annum is insufficient to calculate the annual labour cost. If just one copy of a master is taken, total time is 18 seconds made up of:

Lifting lid, placing master	8 secs
Running time	4 secs
Removing master and copy	6 secs

    For multiple copies, only the running time increases (4 seconds per copy). A sample of one morning's work gave the following breakdown for 336 copies.

Number of copies	1	2	3	4	5	'10'	'20'	'30'	'50'
Frequency	50	15	8	3	2	7	3	1	1
Time per job (secs)	18	22	26	30	34	54	94	134	214

This totals 43 minutes work per morning which, when supplemented with paper loading and dealing with copies stuck in the machine, gives approximately 50 minutes' work. Fifty minutes' work per morning for 336 copies gives approximately 450 hours per annum for 180,000 copies.

These 450 hours were charged at a secretary's gross labour cost of £2.2/hour. The photocopier was used by higher-wage employees in the organisation but it would be wrong to use these higher wages when working out the labour costs associated with the photocopier as it is up to the organisation to use its labour effectively.

Revenues

Revenues from a product sold direct to a customer   The easiest revenues to estimate are those charged at a flat rate for a single product, invoiced directly to a customer (for example a car wash, or a coin-operated washing machine).

Complications arise where there are:

(1) *discounts* for bulk orders. This is common in the printing and plastics industries, indeed anywhere with a relatively high set-up cost.

(2) *surcharges* for adding extra features to a standard model. This is common in consumer durables, especially new vehicles, and in the provision of services (e.g. hairdressing and dental treatment).

(3) a significant number of *offcuts, seconds, rejects* or *imperfects* produced. This is found for example in the clothing and pottery industries. Initially these items might have been sold off on an *ad hoc* basis. Sometimes it becomes a permanent marketing ploy to have such goods available, and a machine's profitability suffers because it is devoting more of its thoughput to stuff with a low profit margin. Although a particular machine's profits may fall by having to make seconds, the machines's owners might benefit (because, for example, there might be a much faster turnover of the inferior goods which reduces distribution and stocking costs).

Connected to the inferior-goods phenomenon is the so-called *by-products* situation. For example, in an oil refinery, gas oil has the sulphur removed from it to make it a less pungent product. The principal purpose of the extraction process is to produce pure gas oil. It is only incidental that a by-product, sulphur, emerges, bringing in a small revenue.

An extension of the by-product situation is where you have many *joint products* made simultaneously by the same machine (e.g. a crude-oil distillation tower, an automatic loom or a continuous paper-mill). Market forces might make first one, then another product dominant (for example, the most valuable products from an oil refinery have been, at various times, paraffins, gasolines, fuel oils or petrochemicals). When it is perceived that there has been a permanent change in the market, the refinery attempts to adjust its processing machinery to make more of the dominant product. Sometimes the market changes are so great that even the most modern and efficient processing equipment has to be closed down.

'Revenues' from a product of an intermediate machine in a series of processes Consider a large firm such as a steelworks. Usually the value of inputs arriving at the firm and the value of outputs leaving the firm are accurately known. But within such a firm there may be a complex network of machines passing material between themselves. This material is known as *intermediate stock* or *work in progress*. How can such material be valued?

Sometimes the price of an intermediate material is known because there is an active market for it (e.g. steel bars). Sometimes you are mistaken in wanting to know the value of inputs and outputs because they will not affect the particular decision that you are worried about. If it is necessary to make an evaluation, it is best to do this only for a group of machines between inputs and outputs of known values.

Intangible benefits Some machines — even those supplying a service direct to a final consumer — produce an 'intangible' revenue, (e.g. a lift, an escalator, a traffic-light system or hospital equipment). The first step is to ask yourself whether there is any non-monetary measure of the machine's effectiveness: for a lift, the number of people using it; for traffic lights, x more cars taking y less minutes to traverse a road-section; for a cancer-therapy machine, x patients living y more years. When such data have been assembled, you might have a clearer picture of the social value of a machine (if social value can be measured). Some cost–benefit analysts claim that all these intangibles can be converted to money terms, but this is open to dispute.

Contact Exercise

1. Visit a machine with which you are unfamiliar.
2. Find out as much as you can about the inputs, outputs, throughputs, costs and revenues.
3. Write a report which summarises your findings. You will

need to contact someone who owns or runs such a machine. Contacting these people can be a problem because:

(i) service engineers are elusive (they are always on the move);
(ii) operatives' work may be so demanding that they can't stop and talk to you;
(iii) machines can be noisy, dusty, hot, dangerous and inaccessible.

Our experience is that *if* you manage to get through to someone responsible for a machine they are usually delighted to tell you about it.

The 'Standard Alternative' Approach to Decisions

All decisions about a machine must be made with some imperfect information. The many reasons for this have been outlined in our review of costs and revenues above. But the problem of missing or doubtful information can be overcome if you compress decision making to a choice between standardised alternatives. To take an obvious example, if you are comparing two cars with the same fuel efficiency, future changes in the price of petrol may be ignored. Likewise, if you are comparing two chemical-extractors, so long as they handle the same input, it doesn't matter that there are awkward problems in valuing this input. And, if you are comparing two machines which take up the same space, you don't have to worry about the allocation of rent and rates by Head Office to these machines as you intend to ignore these overhead allocations in the comparison.

Therefore, to make an effective evaluation of alternatives, eliminate everything that is common to both alternatives and concentrate on the rest. The detailed breakdown of costs and revenues previously given helps you to do this. The more difficult the decision, the more appropriate is this procedure. The replacement decision in particular benefits from such an approach. Unless you are careful, replacement decisions fail to compare like with like, especially with respect to time spans. For example, when comparing machine A (with an optimal life of 3 years) to machine B (with an optimal life of 5 years), it helps to take the common denominator of 15 years as the basis for comparison.

Example of Comparative Analysis of Machines: Case for Purchasing a Rapier rather than a Shuttle Loom (an extract)

Savings on running costs   Choice of a rapier loom will result in substantial savings in material, labour and replacement parts:

Figure 3.5   Wilson and Longbottom rapier loom

(1) Material savings of up to 5 per cent are anticipated mainly from less
    waste. A shuttle loom changes pirns approximately every 15 seconds
    with a weft-waste loss of some 4 per cent of total fabric weight. Con-
    tinuous weft feed of the rapier loom eliminates this problem as well
    as making the selvedges (side edges) tidier. (A pirn is the bobbin of
    wet yarn that fits inside a shuttle.)
(2) Labour savings of up to 50 per cent in total are anticipated from two
    areas:
    (i)   pirn winding — this operation is not required for the rapier loom;
    (ii) weaving — the loom has a significantly higher production rate.
(3) Replacement parts savings of up to 25 per cent are anticipated. Shuttle
    looms are heavier on replacement parts (particularly shuttles and pirns)
    than rapier looms and the pirn winding process is not now required.

Further Reading

Standard Texts

Harding (1984) Chapters IX, X.
Lewis (1981) Chapters 10, 11.
Mayer (1975) Appendix A.

Specialist Texts

How Things Work (1972) vols 1 and 2, Paladin. The workings of modern-day machines, graphically explained.

Pirsig,R.M. (1974) *Zen and the Art of Motorcycle Maintenance*, Corgi. Not such a joke as it sounds. This cult novel gives some useful insights into the systems approach to machines. Note particularly his comments on Phaedrus's knife.

Case Studies

Meier (1982) Transcontinental.
Schmenner (1986) Dean's Brewery.

Chapter 4

PEOPLE

Objectives and Corporate Culture

'Objectives' are the broad, long-range, important goals that an organisation's workers mutually agree to achieve. If an organisation is not sure about its objectives, then there is danger of confusion from the boardroom to the shopfloor. So it is worth summarising what these objectives usually are, and how they affect operations management.

Firstly, those with power to influence a firm's top-level decision making negotiate to achieve a balance between these corporate objectives:

(i)   the maximum dividend to distribute
(ii)   capital appreciation of shares
(iii)   dominance over competitors
(iv)   community approval
(v)   political influence
(vi)   employee satisfaction
(vii)   growth through acquisitions

These corporate objectives determine the middle-management objectives of departmental heads and white-collar professionals:

(i)   ability to meet a deadline
(ii)   maintenance of high quality output
(iii)   curbing of excessive costs

Beneath middle-management objectives are shopfloor objectives, operated by personnel department and employee's supervisors:

(i)   high productivity
(ii)   high skill and proficiency
(iii)   low absenteeism and labour turnover

(iv)   low rates of industrial disputes
(v)   willingness to accept job flexibility

In effective organisations, everyone is in accord about objectives, at whatever level.

Such organisations are said to have a good corporate culture. 'Culture' in this context refers to the noticeable way in which *all* work is done by *all* workers in an organisation; for example the strong customer-orientation at MacDonald's Hamburger Chain or Scandinavian Airline Services. A review of US customer-orientated firms can be found in Peters and Waterman's *In Search of Excellence*. In Britain, the transition to a good new culture was achieved by John Harvey-Jones, Chairman of ICI. To an outsider it would appear that subsidiaries were given much more responsibility so long as they achieved certain profit targets. Taking a cursory glance inside ICI you would notice that the central bureaucracy was being dismantled and a new budgetary system installed. An even closer look at the *people* would reveal a general letting-down of hair and greater nonconformity.

Emphasis on corporate culture has been put forward as a major reason for the success of Japanese firms. When these firms set up subsidiaries in other parts of the world they lay great store on establishing a good culture. For example when Nissan set up a new factory in Washington, County Durham, they considered 17,000 applicants before choosing 250 manu-facturing staff with the special qualities they were looking for. Nissan wished to operate a system of flexible innovation. All employees were to be involved in a cycle of *planning, doing, checking* and *actioning*. Within each of these categories were subcycles. This system, more extensive than Quality Circles, is known as *'Kaizen'* (continual improvement).

Management Control and Communications

Most large organisations have an *organisation chart* which identifies every worker's boss. An example of such a chart is shown in Figure 4.1.

Identifying the span of control   For any boss on the organisation chart, this is measured by the number of subordinates he has got. There is no hard-and-fast rule on the ideal number of subordinates. It varies from industry to industry and on whether there is an assembly, batch, continuous or service process. With close, one-to-one training (e.g. in dentistry), the span of control is at most two or three. With experienced workers doing routine jobs on trouble-free and simple operations, it can be 40+.

The role of cross-departmental links   Organisation charts emphasise authority, command, responsibility and supervision. They are **not** meant

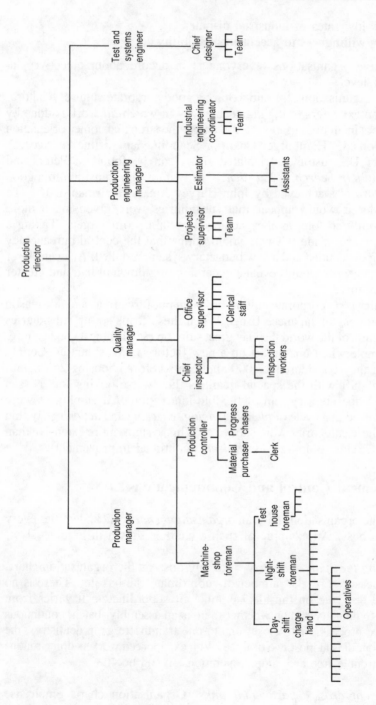

Figure 4.1 Organisation chart

to define other types of contact. There should be an unhindered flow of information between many departments of a firm, even if they are only remotely connected on the organisation chart. For example, marketing with quality assurance, transport with packaging, progress chasers with production control, personnel with supervisors.

Communicating with colleagues   Consider boss – subordinate communications. There are distinct styles.

	Boss to subordinate	Subordinate replies
(a) *Participatory*	Very interesting. What are we going to do about it?	Let us do this and this and start next week.
(b) *Delegatory*	Could you have a go at doing this yourself?	Leave it to me. I'll look after it.
(c) *Audit*	Have you done what was wanted?	Up to a point. I'll explain what I have done.
(d) *Boundary etiquette*	I gather your work is being held up by another department.	Please could you speak to someone about it.
(e) *Bureaucratic*	Our project has to go through many stages of approval.	My committee will collect detailed evidence and start work on all the necessary reports.

People who want to get things done prefer styles (a) and (b). But other styles *occasionally* have their advantages. For example, style (e) would be suitable for the launching of a new drug with possibly dangerous side-effects.

Communicating with outsiders   Some security-conscious firms try to minimise or formalise such contacts. This is to stop theft, bribery, the leaking of trade secrets or adverse publicity, or to stop poaching of employees. Apart from these exceptional situations, there is much to be said for encouraging outside contacts. It is an essential part of a salesman's duty to go beyond regular customers and to make *cold contacts* with people he has never met before. Likewise a purchasing officer should actively be seeking new suppliers, especially where a firm has only one current source. Training of apprentices can often be supplemented in technical colleges. It is also useful to have access to subcontractors who can help you handle an unexpected surge in orders.

Jobs and Conditions of Work

Most established workers have a contract of employment. Sometimes this contract is spelt out into a more detailed job description:

(i)   as a reminder where the employee has a variety of duties (some done only infrequently);

(ii)   as a means of drawing a clear boundary between who does what, where the employee's responsibilities might overlap with those of neighbouring colleagues;

(iii)   when it is necessary to draw up detailed linkages showing communication or authority;

(iv)   when it is used as the basis for appraising an employee's performance.

That is the good news. The bad news is that in large organisations where personnel departments have been established for some time, job descriptions get out of hand. Fairly straightforward job descriptions tend to get written up exhaustively and tend to become a mixture of *responsibilities, skills, procedures, roles* and *initiatives*.

Job design   Certain strenuous jobs are essential for the operation of our society − e.g. firemen, policemen, and soldiers in a battle situation.

Clearly a manager responsible for such strenuous jobs should take care in designing conditions of work. Here is a three-phase approach to this problem:

(1) *Phase 1*   Take every nasty feature of a job and apply a rough unpleasantness scale (the exercise on p. 53 shows one way of doing this).

(2) *Phase 2*   Write out a rough job description which clearly distinguishes the five features *responsibilities, skills, procedures, roles,* and *initiatives*.

(3) *Phase 3*   Work out a satisfactory scheme of remuneration and fulfilment. This may not be easy.

Money alone is not sufficient compensation for the job that has to be done. One alternative is job rotation, where the dirtiest jobs are shared. Or there may be other non-monetary rewards, such as high recognition by society for firemen or policemen in the thick of activity. Or there may be early retirement and generous pensions for the most strenuous jobs. Or there may be a granting of independence and freedom from supervision. Finally, there may be a generous system of off-work allowances, longer holidays or more breaks for relaxation and recovery.

Exercise

Choose two occupations listed in Figure 4.2. For each occupation use the three-phase approach in order to design equitable conditions of work. Here is the unpleasantness scale we suggest you use for Phase 1. For any occupation, fill in a complete column of unpleasantness factors.

0 No trouble, or not relevant.
1 Could be some bad effects in the long run, but fairly minor.
2 Unhygienic for the particular row characteristic in question.
3 Not only unhygienic but positively dangerous for this particular row characteristic.
4 Not only dangerous but potentially deadly.

	Inner-city police officer	Sewerman	Deep-sea fisherman	Miner (face worker)	Removal man	Abattoir worker	Infantryman (wartime)	Publican	Dustbin man	Lumberjack
General fatigue										
Muscle/posture strain										
Eye/nerve strain										
Wetness										
Noise										
Temperature										
Smell/foul air										
Chemical contamination										
Accident danger										
Monotony										
Other										

Figure 4.2 Job design pro forma

Payment Systems

Introduction

All payments systems can be divided into four types:

(i)   payment for the number of hours worked;
(ii)   payment for the number of items made;
(iii)   a share of the profits;
(iv)   a fixed payment for fulfilling the duties of a post.

This is a deceptively simple classification. Any firm that has formulated its wage agreement with a union will need to write out a document the length of a small book. The complications arise through a tendency to have:

(i)   a different wage for each craft, skill or profession;
(ii)   a different reward for each different product made under piecework;
(iii)   different allowances for the many circumstances under which work takes place.

Payment systems must also be tailored to the particular operating process in question. A research laboratory functions better using profit sharing and fixed payments rather than payment by number of hours or number of items. This last type of payment would also not be suitable for a worker on a fixed-pace assembly line, but would be ideal where measurable work is required from building subcontractors. Payment for the number of hours worked would be suitable where the worker is required as much for his or her *presence* as for the *content* of what he does (as, for example, with a nightwatchman or artist's model). As most organisations have a mixture of processes, they tend to have a mixture of payment systems too.

Faced with such a complexity, are there any general guiding principles underlying payment policies? Put banally, a firm wants to give the worker an incentive to do what the firm wants that worker to do. Often, this has been crudely translated as 'How can we get the worker to maximise his output rate per hour?' More subtly, one seeks a payment system that also meets other objectives, such as high quality of finished work, low labour turnover and absenteeism, or an innovative and loyal workforce.

Time-rates of Payment

When people are paid a basic *hourly rate* or a *day rate*, what exceptions and adjustments must be covered?

(i)   the *overtime rate*, according to whether it is longer working hours during the weekday, nightwork, other awkward hours during shiftwork, weekend working, or working over a statutory holiday — overtime rates traditionally appear as 1¼, 1½, or double-time mark-ups;

(ii) *differentials*, to take into account the different profession, competence, experience and status of every worker in an organisation;

(iii) *special allowances* for: living in a certain geographic area (e.g. an isolated community, a capital city, or a war-zone); unsocial duties (e.g. a fireman handling dangerous chemicals, a policeman handling dangerous people); or doing duty outside the normal terms of contract (e.g. emergency-replacement or training others).

All of the above have to be changed every time there is a general cost-of-living increase. Such change can lead to *wage-drift*, a state of affairs where these 'extras' become a larger proportion of a worker's earnings. On the surface, wage-drift may appear fairly harmless. But in the long-run it can have a bad effect on the workforce's attitude and productivity. For example, they might surreptitiously 'go slow' during normal hours to increase work needing to be done during overtime.

Time-rate payment systems do not by themselves encourage people to work hard. So such systems have to be supplemented with close (and expensive) supervision, with disciplinary procedures to keep the bad workers on their toes, and with promotion procedures to give an incentive to the good. As well as such systems being administratively complicated, they do not permit finer, subtler elements of control of workers. Ideally, a 'reward and punishment' approach works best if it is applied in small doses, follows directly from the cause, and is an intimate matter between supervisor and worker. It is hard to get time-rate systems to work in this way.

Piece-rate and Variants

In its crudest form, piece-rate rewards are directly proportional to the output a worker produces, as shown in Figure 4.3.

The crude proportional piece-rate system is still popular with sub-contractors, outworkers and commission salesmen. But most piece-rates include certain enhancements, summarised in Figure 4.4.

Stabilising incentive schemes   If output is subject to erratic fluctuations, only partly under the influence of the worker, this can have drastic effects on a pieceworker's earnings. One way of stabilising earnings is to arrange for them to be based on a moving average of a worker's performance (for example on his or her last three months' work). This certainly damps down

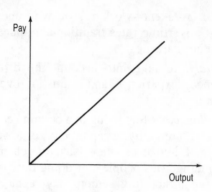

Figure 4.3

extreme fluctuations, but it also creates a lag between the worker's effort and the reward received for it.

Another approach is to devise a league table of workers. The highest rates per hour are given to those 'First Division' workers with the highest rate of productivity. Typically there may be eight to twelve divisions. Promotion and demotion between divisions is determined by a moving average often based over the last month's performance. Unlike in a football league, there is no fixed number of people in each division. All employees may be in the top (or bottom) division. But the rules prevent a new employee leaping from bottom to top division straight away: however good the performance, he or she can only be promoted to the division immediately above. The length of time it will take to claw all the way up to the top division is supposed to condition the worker to hard work. It is usual for a fall-off in performance to be treated a little leniently (e.g. at any review a worker may fall by no more than one, or sometimes two, divisions). This league-table procedure is a frequent feature of measured daywork piece-rate systems.

Overview of piece-rate systems   Wherever a worker's output can be easily measured, management should give serious consideration to a piece-rate system. But when doing so, they should take cognisance of a whole range of possible negative effects:

(i)   deterioration in quality;
(ii)   extra administrative costs in calculating piece-rate payments;
(iii)   work study having to calculate a new piece-rate each time there is an operating improvement;
(iv)   pieceworkers hiding any improvements they make to their job in order to avoid having their rate cut;

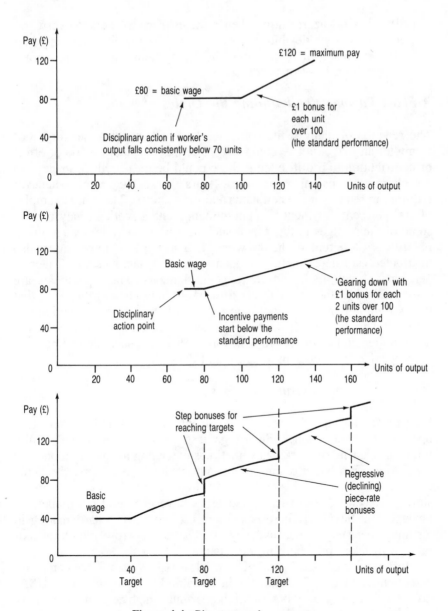

Figure 4.4 Piece-rate enhancements

(v)   pieceworkers' preference for a big queue of incoming work, encouraging high in-process stocks;

(vi)   discontent if a carelessly designed piece-rate system gives easy money to some;

(vii)   health hazards if greed encourages piece workers to overwork;

(viii)   loss of job flexibility — workers will be unwilling to train others or to substitute on a job where they cannot immediately reach a high level of productivity.

A Fixed Payment for Fulfilling the Duties of a Job

The rewards of many white-collar workers fall into this category. For example, an MP is not — could not — be paid by hours worked, effort or contribution to profit, even if these could be measured. Managers do not claim extra payment for out-of-hours work. They work whenever required in return for greater status and job security. These are examples of 100 per cent 'payment by appointment'. Other workers may receive some of their wages in this form, such as a basic minimum wage given regardless of output or hours worked. This type of payment is also distributed via fringe benefits: company car, sports facilities, medical care, pensions, travel, fuel, and clothing entitlements. These payments are distinguished by their availability to workers regardless of the effort that they put into their work. Could more blue-collar workers get paid in this fashion? This happens in Japan and may be one component in securing a committed and co-operative workforce. However such a move must be accompanied by proper motivation and control.

Bonus and Profit-sharing Schemes

Pure profit-sharing schemes are found only among small workers' co-operatives and communes. Such organisations are run on almost family lines, the sharing of workload sometimes extending to sharing money or possessions. For larger organisations, a less intense co-ownership scheme can work well (as, for example, in the John Lewis chain of department stores). Recently, co-ownership schemes have increased in number via management buyouts. There is some risk to employees participating in a management buyout because they often have to borrow at high rates of interest to take up a share in the business.

From the employees' point of view a less risky system is the company-wide bonus scheme. For example the Scanlon Plan, popular in the USA, gives the workers greater bonuses if they maintain high general productivity (e.g. by avoiding excessive overtime or downtime). Another successful scheme in the USA (the Lincoln Electric Plan) succeeds by a subtle mixture of individual, departmental and company bonuses.

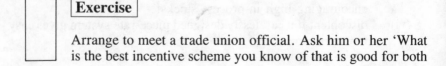

Exercise

Arrange to meet a trade union official. Ask him or her 'What is the best incentive scheme you know of that is good for both

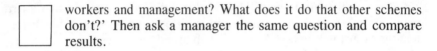

workers and management? What does it do that other schemes
don't?' Then ask a manager the same question and compare
results.

Work Measurement

Output is affected by varying labour, machine and material inputs. By
convention, work measurement concentrates on labour input. A classic
and early example is F.W. Taylor's story of his pig-iron-loading experiments
in Bethlehem, Pennsylvania in 1899 (see Annex to this section). The topic
of work measurement covers a controversial area. It influences the hiring
and firing policy of a firm, the work practices and the level of incentives
and wages. Sometimes, especially in specialist engineering and subcontracting, the measurement of work is delegated to a foreman or rate
fixer. He negotiates with each worker the payment rate for each special
job done. But this would be a laborious, haphazard arrangement in industries
with a more regular pattern of work. In such industries measurements made
well in advance can be used again and again as a basis for payment, supervision and job design. These measurements are the province of the work-
study personnel.

The tools of a traditional work-study officer were elementary: stopwatch
and clipboard. Officers had to have an intimate knowledge of all jobs that
they examined, and empathy with the workers whom they observed. Also,
they were valued for their experience in fairly judging the correct pace
of work, allowing for workers' different abilities and different working
conditions. Nowadays there is a tendency to replace, or rather enhance,
the work-study officer's experience with more formal methods of analysis.
This may require detailed physiological knowledge or access to a computer
data base. Consultants are often brought in to install a proprietary work-
measurement system and to instruct work-study personnel in its operation.
To appreciate the more complex work-measurement systems it is a good
idea to understand the broader, simpler systems from which they have
developed. So here we will consider work measurement via a series of
levels, from the broadest to the most detailed.

Level 1: Long-run Productivity Measurements

These are usually derived from accounting data, and are normally prepared
yearly, but occasionally quarterly, monthly or weekly. They may refer
to a whole company or to a division, factory or department within it. In
its simplest form:

$$\text{Productivity} = \frac{\text{Physical volume of output}}{\text{Number of employees}}$$

It is not difficult to spot flaws in this definition. Suppose that a firm makes a variety of products measured in different units (tons, cubic metres, lengths or just numbers)? Also, do such broad measures tell you anything about how workers alone are improving their performance? More often, these productivity measures change because of redundancies, or the introduction of capital-intensive machinery. Also, any business could improve its 'productivity' by cutting its quality or product range. So productivity, crudely defined, should not be used as *the* decision-making criterion.

Level 2: Activity Sampling over Days or Weeks

This involves taking snap observations of an employee, typically over one or two weeks but longer if a high degree of accuracy is required. The objective is to use the sample of snap observations as an estimate of the complete work of the employee. In designing an exercise, the first requirement is to define a reasonable set of activities. For example, for a milkman such activities would probably include:

- delivering milk
- waiting for payment
- collecting money
- returning empties
- moving to next house
- returning to depot for more milk
- waiting at depot
- unloading empties
- loading fresh milk, etc.
- returning from depot

It is preferable to have clear-cut boundaries for activities. In the example above *waiting for payment* and *collecting money*, and *unloading empties* and *loading fresh milk,* could overlap.

You have to be careful *when* you make your snap observations, as it is easy to introduce bias. An observer might be tempted to omit a recording early or late in the day, or during the lunch hour. A ritualistic observer might take recordings 'on the hour' and therefore give too much weight to shift changes which are more likely to occur at this point. Random sampling may lead to awkward short gaps between recordings, or a 'dead time' within which the observer cannot get on with anything else. Also too short a gap between recordings may lead to an unacceptably frequent similarity between the two successive activities involved.

Activity sampling is most relevant where there are organisational objections to continuous observation and/or where continuous observation is too expensive. Activity sampling is obviously unsuitable where there is difficulty arranging to make an observation (e.g. down a sewer) or where the nature of the work makes it very difficult to classify what is happening (e.g. writing a computer program). It is also unsuitable where the intermittent arrival of the work-study officer disrupts the employee's work (e.g. calling in on a secondary-school teacher and distracting the class).

It should also be noted that activity sampling is an inefficient way of gathering information about predictable activities (e.g. when a doctor is holding his regular surgery) or even semi-predictable ones (e.g. the daily pigeon-holing of a department's incoming mail).

Quite a few examples of the application of activity sampling refer to jobs where bottlenecks, queuing or waiting are a noticeable feature (e.g. receptionists, retailing staff, secretaries, storekeepers). Care should be taken before deciding to use activity sampling to analyse these jobs. If you are particularly interested in the dangers of overload, when for example a queue is beyond a certain length, use the queuing theory approach of Operational Research rather than activity sampling.

Level 3: Measurements from Daily Operating Information

In the day-to-day running of the workplace, certain paperwork passes between operatives, foremen and the production-control staff: works orders, job tickets, machine routing-and-loading instructions, material requisitions, starting and completion dates, labour usages, and inspection and delivery cards. For example, a plastic-injection-moulding unit which is run well should be able to supply a work-study officer with this information, without necessitating extra observations on the shopfloor.

Analysis of machine downtime

Shift start-up preparations
End-of-work clearing up
Testing machine specifications
New mould installation
Old mould removal
Repair
Waiting for repair
Waiting for material
Waiting for operative
Waiting for a job

Labour information

Name of operative
Basic hours worked
Overtime hours worked
Hours assigned to each machine

Job information

Name of customer
Work order-code
Size of order
Due delivery date
Mould-preparation time
Material-loading time
Cure/press time

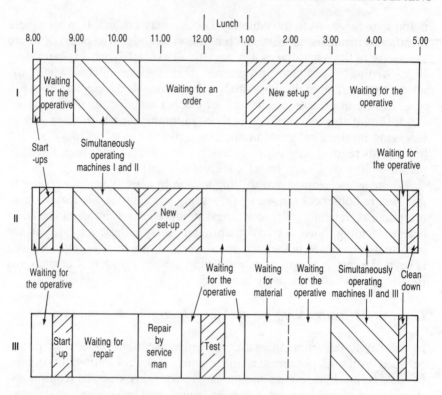

Figure 4.5   Activities of an injection-moulding operative

Even with all such information it is difficult for a work-study officer to construct the *sequence* of happenings during the day. For this purpose it is necessary to have a diary of events for the operative and each of the machines under his or her control. This information can be compressed into a resource-utilisation bar chart. The charts in Figure 4.5 show the activities of an injection-moulding operative responsible for three machines: I, II and III. The shaded areas pinpoint which machine the operative is working on at any point of the day.

Day-to-day information in this form is of great interest to the work-study officer and to production control. It helps them come to decisions about manpower planning, job structuring and productivity improvements. But at this (still broad) level of detail it is inefficient to have someone collecting records by keeping a permanent watch on the workers. During the day there are still relatively few occasions when a note has to be made that a change in activity has taken place. It is preferable if the worker directly involved or the foreman, rather than work study, records this data. Carrying out extra clerical duties will be a nuisance to machine operatives, and understandably their records are often not as accurate or complete as work study would like. As a general rule, you would expect better feedback from workers who feel that they are part of the decision-making process.

Level 4: Cycles of Work within a Day

Within a day, a worker may move repetitively between machines or jobs. Typically, such a cycle of activities could take between 1 and 20 minutes. This situation can be observed in a wide variety of industrial practices, particularly in the machining of metal or wood, in garment manufacture and on many assembly lines. Certain of these situations are worth analysing via a *multiple-activity chart* if the following conditions hold:

(i) the worker can easily transfer his attention backwards and forwards between distinct machines, processes or products;

(ii) there are occasions when a machine runs automatically, freeing the attendant to work elsewhere for a while.

Consider the previous plastic-injection-moulding example. The operative was moving between three machines:

(i) loading/unloading them; or
(ii) letting them work automatically on curing; or
(iii) leaving the machines idle.

The products have the characteristics shown in Table 4.1. On the basis of these characteristics, the multiple-activity chart shown in Figure 4.6 was drawn up.

Table 4.1 Product characteristics (times in minutes)

	Loading/ unloading	Automatic curing	Total
Product A on Machine I	2	4	6
Product B on Machine II	1	2	3
Product C on Machine III	1	1	2

In day-to-day matters, it is the production-control staff who make most use of multiple-activity charts. The scheduling aspect of their work is described elsewhere. But the charts also provide a useful basis for certain work-study exercises:

(i) to provide information for the tackling of long-term bottleneck problems − by analysing many charts, one can discover whether

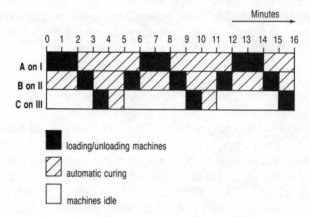

Figure 4.6 Operator's multiple-activity chart developed from product characteristics

it is better to research into ways to cut loading/unloading times, or whether it is better to try to speed up curing times;

(ii)   to consider the options for job structure and design — workers might find certain switching between machines too boring or too stressful.

This is exercise

Level 5: Job Elements within a Cycle

Consider the duties of a woman responsible for clearing dirty plates etc. from the tables of a canteen. Setting out from the kitchen area she has this cycle of activities:

(i)   push trolley from kitchen area to first uncleared table;
(ii)   go through a *sub-cycle* of activities (see later) to clear that table.
(iii)   if trolley is full, return to kitchen area; otherwise
(iv)   push trolley to next uncleared table, and go to (ii) above.

Within activity (ii) is a further sub-cycle of activities:

(i)   collect uneaten food and rubbish and put it in the trolley's bin;
(ii)   collect cutlery and place in trolley bins;
(iii)   collect cups and glasses and place on top of trolley;
(iv)   collect plates and stack underneath trolley;
(v)   clear trays with a cloth and take to nearest stack of trays;
(vi)   wipe table clean with a cloth.

Each of the above activities is close to what in traditional work study was known as a *job element*. In its purest form, a job element embraces everything within a uniform activity, for example:

- climbing a ladder of a certain height and slope
- lifting a load of a certain weight to a certain height
- screwing up a nut on a certain length bolt

It is convenient to relax this definition a little to include an activity which contains a messy set of slightly variable operations but which is nevertheless quite distinct − clearing rubbish from a table is a good example of this.

The recording process also has an influence on how job elements are defined. It is useful if the observer can collect times at reasonable intervals (say between 5 and 30 seconds). One looks for a clear *breakpoint* which separates two job elements and can be used as a signal to record a time. The breakpoint may be something obviously separating elements, such as a van door being slammed shut. But an observer might also want to use something which, although quite clear to him (e.g. an operator's regular turn of his head), nevertheless does not strictly divide two elements.

Very often, job elements are being used as the building blocks in exercises to determine people's workloads and rates of pay. Therefore a work-study officer must be aware of subtle variations in the nature of work and somehow make allowances for them. For example, the canteen worker will be affected by:

(i)   *object resistance* − e.g. the extra power required to accelerate and brake a heavily loaded as distinct from an empty trolley;

(ii) *object fragility* − the greater care required if you have a higher proportion of glasses to collect;

(iii) *object shape* − e.g. cups are easier to pick up than saucers but more difficult to stack.

Also the woman in the canteen will be affected by environmental variations outside her control, e.g:

(iv) *variations in efficiency of tools* − e.g. jammed swivels on a trolley's wheel so that it won't go smoothly round corners;

(v)   *physical blocks to efficiency* − e.g. briefcases blocking passageways;

(vi) *physical environment* − e.g. too hot, too cold, too dark;

(viii) *mental distractions* − a loose child, dog, or wasp.

It is essential for a work-study officer to be aware of the above hindrances. They affect how he or she *rates the performance* of the person being observed. If it is judged to be slower than a normal well-motivated worker, then the *observed time* is scaled down to a *basic time*. Scaling down is a subjective issue depending entirely on the skill and experience of the work-study officer. This is aided by _tempo-rating_ — observing films of workers operating at a variety of performance levels and comparing observers' assessments. Eventually, if observers do enough tempo-rating exercises, their estimates should converge.

Various allowances are added to the basic time to arrive at a final _standard time_ for a job. These allowances are:

(i)   _personal allowances_ — e.g. refreshment or toilet breaks;
(ii) _fatigue allowances_ — e.g. rests after heavy lifting or a long period of concentration;
(iii) _delay or contingency allowances_ — e.g. where the system has broken down and there is a material, staff, machine or vehicle shortage;
(iv) _interference allowance_ — e.g. where there is enforced idleness even when the system is working optimally. This idleness arises from the technical nature of the process, such as waiting for a chemical mixture to settle, or for a machine to decelerate before the next job can be done.

Work study can make objective recommendations as to what these allowances should be. Often they are amended as a result of bargaining between unions and management. So actual allowances for the same job may vary from firm to firm depending on union and management bargaining power.

Exercise

1. With two colleagues go out and find a self-service petrol station.
2. Position yourself so that you will not interfere with the running of the station but make sure that you can observe the customer's activities.
3. Watch a customer throughout his visit to the station from the moment he enters the station to the moment he rejoins the road. Divide the customer's activities into about ten job elements with clear breakpoints separating them.
4. Get yourself organised with clipboard, pen and a watch with a second-recorder. Note down when a customer reaches each breakpoint during his stay at the station. Observe between 15 and 20 customers.
5. Then carry out a simple statistical analysis:
   (a) What is the average time for a complete visit?
   (b) What is the average time for each job element within this visit?

(c) Look at the distribution of times around each average that you have found. What do these distributions look like? For each job element are they: (i) packed closely to the average or widely dispersed; (ii) skewed on one side of the average rather than the other?

(d) If you know about 'normal' and 'poisson' distributions you could test whether your results fit in closely with either of these. But you might well have discovered another type of distribution.

(e) Review you results and try to provide a logical reason for them.

6. Did the customers mind being observed? Do you think that if you had been timing a person in paid employment, there would have been different reactions?

Level 6: Micro-movement within a Job Element

Self-generated data Typically, job elements occur within the frequency range of 2–20 a minute. But there are situations where it is desirable to make a much greater breakdown of an employee's movements, in extreme cases up to 200 per minute. This can be done by taking a film of an employee, and analysing his motions frame by frame. For many firms, the cost of film equipment used to be regarded as prohibitive, but nowadays quite a moderate budget can obtain a cine camera and video recording equipment.

Predetermined data An alternative to taking your own film is to call upon the experience of micromotion consultants, especially those offering variants of Methods Time Measurement (MTM). From the analysis of enormous numbers of slow-motion films, they have constructed detailed reference tables. These cover pretty well every physical activity that an employee could make, permed against such things as the weight of material to be lifted, the distance over which the object moves and the outside characteristics of the object. Most micromotion systems start from a major classification of motions similar to Gilbreth's 18 'Therbligs' (see the Annex to Method Study). But within these major lines are sub-classifications and within them sub-sub-classifications. Altogether, the MTM tables cover thousands of different situations. Even so, you have to do a lot of observation and preparatory work before you can take advantage of the MTM tables.

Consider the actions of a canteen lady from the moment she stops her trolley by an uncleared table to the moment she grasps a dirty plate two seconds later. The following list gives the *minimum* detail that you are required to assemble before starting an MTM analysis. The italicised headings on the left-hand side refer to the major classifications of motion. On the right-hand site you get an idea of the further detail that must be provided. There are shorthand codes for summarising this detail.

Eye   *Glance* travels from trolley to table, 2.5 m, and *focuses* on a dirty plate 2.5 metres away from the eye
Body   *Straightens from stooping* position (the stoop resulting from having pushed the trolley)
Body   *Turns* 90 degrees
Legs   *Walk* four steps at 'obstructed' pace due to chairs in way
Reach   At (jumbled classification) dirty plate Left hand 0.4 m
Grasp   Dirty plate (classed as a light, fragile, flat cylinder, 0.2 m in diameter with interference to grasp underneath)

At first sight analysing any job in such detail seems ridiculous. And yet there are two very important applications for this technique:

(1) Where the employee has to show tremendous manual dexterity to avoid a disastrous consequence (e.g. a power-plant operator, pilot or surgeon). Such work has been extensively analysed in *ergonomic laboratories*.
(2) Where there is a repetitive operation using a universal machine (e.g. driving a vehicle, operating a lathe, working a sewing machine). In these cases, a costly MTM study can be justified in view of the many man-years that a firm's employees might spend operating these machines.

Exercise

Carry out a micromotion analysis of some simple common activity, such as tying a shoelace, buying a bus ticket, washing up a cup or starting a car.

Annex to Work Measurement: A Return to the Ingot-Loading Project at Bethlehem Steel, 1899

The first proper scientific analysis of manual work is usually credited to Frederick Winslow Taylor. Because Taylor has had such a strong influence on the way in which work study has developed, it is enlightening to look closely at the structure of his most famous illustration.

In *Scientific Management*, Taylor devotes much space to the way in which he improved the productivity of workers whose job was to load railcars with 92-pound ingots of pig-iron. Taylor gives enough data for us to repeat his experiment. A description of the operation is deceptively simple. Piles of ingots were stacked in a field next to a railway line. Loaders were required to pick up an ingot, walk or run up an inclined plank leaning against the side of the railcar, drop the ingot in the railcar and return to repeat the operation. We are told that the average distance from lift to drop was 36 ft. From this minimal information is it possible to set up a similar work-study exercise? What equipment and arrangements are needed?

The railcar   If you do not have access to the real thing in a quiet railway siding use any level staging, platform or bank about 3 ft above ground-floor level.

The loads to be used   If ingots are difficult to obtain, weightlifting weights or heavy stones will do instead. Loads less than 92 lbs may be used if you wish to avoid the risk of injury. More bulky, less rigid items may also be used, such as sacks of sand or cement. In an extended exercise it is interesting to consider variations in weight or bulk on the throughput rate. By a system of returning loads to the starting point (explained later) it is possible to run an experiment with only two 'ingots'.

The planks   Find two planks that can be used as ramps up to your simulated railcar. Any length of plank can be taken, although in later exercises you might like to consider the effect of steepness and 'bendability'. Place the two planks against the 'railcar floor', far enough apart so that one can be used for loading and the other for simultaneous unloading without the two handlers obstructing each other. Also, take precautions to stop the planks slipping when the handlers are running up and down them.

The pig-iron handlers   Seek volunteers a day or so in advance of the exercise. Explain that you do not want super-athletes − just people who can perform heavy manual work under a variety of instructions. Make sure that they have no illness or injury and advise them to avoid eating a heavy meal just before the exercise. You will need two handlers for each exercise that is run. It is possible that the same two volunteers will be able to perform all the exercises that you set up, although you might like to avoid a fatigue factor by using other pairs.

Operating the experiment   Place one load at a level surface just beyond the top of one of your plank-ramps. Place the other load at ground level 36 ft away at a pick-up point. Organise the experiment this way. Whilst one person is carrying a load uphill, the other is simultaneously carrying the other load (via the other plank) back to the pick-up point. After the

two handlers drop their loads, they walk back empty-handed to their starting
points and repeat the cycle.

Collecting information and comparing results   Use any digital watch to
record times to the nearest second. If there are several independent
observers it is instructive to see how their timings compare. At its simplest,
times should be taken the moment that the handler at the bottom lifts his
load and the moment he lets it go at the railcar end. Initially, run the
experiment for five minutes, asking the handlers to work at a pace they
think could be maintained comfortably all day. Remember to point out
that the uphill handler has a slightly harder task than the downhill handler.
After the five-minute experiment is over, compare results between
observers, then consider some of the following variants:

(i)   varying the loading or unloading height from ankle to knee, waist
        or chest height;

(ii)   working with longer or shorter distances than 36 ft;

(iii)   working with the same distance but varying the length of the
        slope or the stability of the plank;

(iv)   picking up from neatly stacked or jumbled ingots (requiring more
        than two loads);

(v)   dropping the ingots neatly stacked or higgledy-piggledy (re-
        quiring more than two loads);

(vi)   working when the ground, ingot and plank are wet and slimy;

(vii)   comparing a 36-ft straight run with a 36-ft path round corners.

   All of these variants are crucial elements in the analysis. If you fail
to find which variant has a really significant effect on the pace of work,
you could come to the wrong conclusion. What starts as an elementary
exercise turns out to have a remarkable number of complications. But does
that justify Taylor's assertion that 'the science of handling pig-iron is so
great that the man who is fit to handle pig-iron as his daily work cannot
possibly understand that science'? It is worth returning to the Bethlehem
experiments to see how Taylor got on.

   Taylor claimed that his scientific methods of *selection, incentive* and
supervision enabled him to improve the daily loading rates per man from
12½ tons to 47½ tons. At 92 lbs an ingot you need to load 1156 ingots
to clear 47½ tons. As the handlers worked a 10-hour day (without any
lunch break), they would have to shift 115 ingots an hour, or about two
a minute to reach their target. In fact they would have to work a bit faster
than that to allow for brief stoppages. Anyone who has duplicated Taylor's
experiment will be able to confirm that over a short period of time, for
the basic situation, such a rate is perfectly possible. But the rate does not
seem possible with the introduction of some quite mildly adverse factors
mentioned in variants (i) and (vii).

Was Taylor's method a practical long-term solution? Even though America a hundred years ago was a tough, no-nonsense climate for the labouring man, it seems unlikely. One is tempted to ask: why didn't he use hoists for this project?

Method Study

Method Study and the Individual Worker

It is rewarding to start learning this subject by direct experiments. If you can arrange it, below are some suitable activities to investigate:

Outdoors:

Fruit-picking (summer/autumn)
Snow-shovelling (winter)
Vegetable-patch digging (winter/spring)
Lawnmowing (spring/summer)
Hedgecutting (spring/summer/autumn)
Hanging out washing (spring/summer/autumn)

Indoors:

Sandwich making
Repairing a cycle-tyre puncture
Ironing
Wiring a new electrical plug

| Exercise |

1. Arrange for a variety of volunteers to try out the jobs, each for a short period of time (say two minutes each).
2. What is the difference in technique between a skilful and a clumsy worker? Try to identify whether the skilful worker does things:
   (a) in a different sequence
   (b) with different movements
   (c) with greater speed and dexterity.
3. Try to classify all the human activities you have observed (for example *look at, grasp* and *sit* might be three of them).
   Try to identify between ten and twenty of them. When you have finished the exercise, compare your list with Gilbreth's 'Therbligs' (see the Annex to Method Study). With

one or two additions, Therbligs are still being used, implicitly, today. Perhaps you have discovered a worthy addition.

Method Study and Teamwork

Here we are concerned with the best way that small groups can function. For example labouring gangs, quarrymen, forestry workers, restaurant staff, a research laboratory or a software development team. The above are examples of where the workers can control the pace of what they do, and also where how they get on with each other can affect productivity.

Example: Refuse Collection

Consider two basic ways in which this can be done:

Method A   The householder has a metal bin next to his back door. In advance of the dustcart's arrival, two men will be bringing bins from houses to the road edge. Later a dustcart with a driver and two loaders will empty the bins. Some way behind the dustcart one man will be returning the empty bins to the houses.

Method B   On the appointed collection day, the householder places his rubbish in a strong plastic sack by the roadside. As the dustcart drives along the street, three loaders pick up the plastic sacks and throw them into the cart.

How much more efficient is Method B than Method A?
(i)   *Men per dustcart*: Method A requires six men, Method B four men.
(ii)   *Time to clear a given section*: Suppose in a 100-metre stretch of street there are on average 40 bins to pick up, grouped in twos on both sides of the road. Under Method B, this stretch can be covered in 90 seconds or less (assume the dustcart moves continuously at walking pace, the three loaders slinging sacks into the cart as it moves). Under Method A, the stretch will be covered in about 450 seconds (15 seconds for the cart to move between each of the ten stopping points, and 30 seconds at a stopping point for the bins to be automatically hoisted up, emptied and lowered).

Class Exercise *(10 minutes)*

Spell out all the advantages and disadvantages of Methods A and B above from the point of view of (a) the dustmen, and

(b) the householders. How would you choose between A and B if you were the local authority responsible for refuse collection?

Method Study and the Organisation

Traditionally, this was the strict sequence of procedures followed by Method Study:

(1) *Select* This involved good diagnosis. That is, being able to pick out a primary problem which, if solved, would enable secondary problems to be cleared up easily. 'Select' also implied the authority to reject unsuitable assignments. This is a good test of Method Study's credibility with upper management.

(2) *Record* This required skill at modelling the system. The several ways of doing this are shown in Chapter 7 on Systems, including the useful and simple flow-process chart often used in Method Study. Also, 'recording' encompasses skills in both observation and measurement (covered in the Work Measurement section).

(3) *Examine* Method Study developed an extremely comprehensive set of probing questions (for example, Carson's Production Handbook lists over 300 questions for metal manufacture alone). More important than the number of questions was the style in which they were generated, associated with brainstorming and Value Analysis techniques.

(4) *Develop* As in the physical sciences, this involved a cycle of hypothesis formulation, testing and validation.

(5) *Submit* This required mastering the presentation arts and persuasive talents of a consultant.

(6) *Install* This involved project planning skills, an ability to marshall resources and meet deadlines, liaising with equipment and software suppliers, and training people in new methods.

(7) *Maintain* When a new system starts, there should be close supervision and a hot line to the installer. After a while this could be relaxed to evaluation by periodic review. Eventually the objective should be self-monitoring by the operators.

This was a natural sequence for a Method Study if everything ran smoothly. But on many occasions new information, or a sudden change in management objectives will force the study to return to an earlier stage. The following case study demonstrates the difficulty of conducting a smooth-running methods exercise.

CASE STUDY: HARRY BRITTON OF NBD

Richard Lake is a young trainee analyst with Systematics Ltd, management consultants. He has been commissioned to investigate the despatch and transport arrangements of a Yorkshire-based food wholesalers, NBD Ltd. Management's *prime objective* is to install a computer-based system which will give better service than at present, and *which will need less clerical assistance to operate it.*

NBD operates from a large warehouse within easy reach of the M1 and M62. It receives supplies direct from manufacturers and importers. It delivers goods to discount stores, supermarkets and small wholesalers within a radius of approximately 100 miles, using its own fleet of forty 24-ton lorries. Competition from other wholesalers is intense and profitability can be achieved only by maintaining a high turnover and by always being in stock for any item that is required. NBD's survival has hinged on its ability to process any order received before 12.00 noon on one day and to deliver it during working hours on the next. The number of its customers and the volume of its business has steadily increased, necessitating extensions to the warehouse, to the size of its transport fleet and to the range of stocks that it carries.

The ordering of goods coming *into* NBD is the responsibility of the purchasing department. This is run by Keith Jarvis, an ambitious young man with a business studies degree. He previously worked for Systematics Ltd as a junior consultant. He had been a member of a team that had been called in to investigate whether NBD could halve its purchasing staff. Keith showed how this could be done by installing a computerised ordering system. The directors of NBD were so impressed by his enthusiasm that they offered him the position of purchasing manager where he could put his ideas into practice. This he had done most successfully. NBD now has a day-to-day record of every item in stock and a computerised system of re-ordering. This is backed up by a vigorous campaign whereby Jarvis and his staff make repeated checks and phone calls to ensure that all suppliers deliver on the exact date required. Jarvis is not a very popular man, but there is no doubt that he gets things done.

In contrast, the sending of goods *from* NBD's warehouse is organised in a completely different manner. The work is done by the despatch department, run by Harry Britton and his two assistants, Doreen Watkins and Ray Price. Harry Britton is 55 years old and has worked at NBD for 30 years. He has no formal qualifications, having left school at sixteen. In his early days with NBD he was a delivery driver, then after a period of ill-health a fork-lift-truck operator. During a period of staff shortages he worked overtime as a despatch clerk and showed such facility for this work that he was hired permanently in this role. For the last fifteen years he has been despatch manager. His major function is to see that all lorries are loaded correctly and that each driver knows exactly where to go. This enables all lorries to get away from the warehouse early in the morning every day of the week, Monday to Friday.

Harry lives next to the warehouse and arrives for work at 5.30 a.m. every morning. He prepares and hands out journey schedules to the drivers who clock in and depart between 6.00 a.m. and 7.00 a.m. The lorries have been loaded by night-shift workers who use data provided by Harry and his two assistants at the end of the previous day. After the last lorry has departed, Harry goes home for a quick breakfast. He returns at 8.00 a.m. Ray Price arrives at this time and Doreen Watkins arrives an hour later, after she has dropped her children off at school. Up to 11.00 a.m. they are always alert for incoming telephone calls from drivers who might have run into trouble: a breakdown, a traffic hold-up or bad weather. When such situations arise they have to make instantaneous and tricky decisions on re-routing or possibly sending out reserve transport to meet requirements.

From 11.00 a.m. to 3.00 p.m. there is a relatively slack period when Harry and his assistants can start work on allocating loads for the next day. After 3.00 p.m. things get a bit hectic. At this time the accounts department passes on customers' orders which were received that morning and which must be delivered by the next day. This amounts to about 40 per cent of total goods to be despatched. Detailed instructions must be prepared for the night shift on how to load the lorries, and journey schedules must be prepared for the lorry drivers, each of whom will be visiting between two and eight customers perhaps at widely-spaced and awkward-to-find locations. In addition Harry is clocking out drivers who have finished their day's deliveries, collecting delivery notes and informing the maintenance department if any vehicle needs attending to. Doreen Watkins has to stop work at 5.00 p.m.; Ray Price works overtime for two or three nights a week until 7.00 p.m.; Harry is always willing to stay on later, often until 8.00 p.m.

Harry's constitution has been weakened by the long hours

and mental strain of his work. He has high blood pressure, is overweight and coughs a lot. But he never misses a day's work and loves his job. If anything happens to him, NBD will be extremely vulnerable, but so far they have been unable to find a satisfactory solution. Three years ago the company invested £30,000 in computer software which theoretically should have been able to provide an automatic and optimal schedule of route allocations and delivery loads. In spite of determined attempts to implement the system, the project had to be abandoned. Jarvis, the purchasing manager and one of the leading proponents of computerisation, argued that the failure was a result of sabotage by the despatch department and the lorry drivers. Others were not so sure. There is no doubt that when it comes to assessing traffic conditions Harry has a masterful 'ear to the ground' which is far superior to the computer's mode of operation. Also he knows the likes and dislikes of every driver for different sorts of route and can allocate work accordingly. The drivers greatly appreciate his skill and there has not been the slightest trouble with the TGWU since Harry has been despatch manager.

It is noticeable that when Harry is on holiday, even though he arranges this to coincide with a quiet time of year, the despatch system all but breaks down. Tim Miller, who is a most efficient assistant maintenance manager and knows the drivers well, acts as temporary replacement for Harry. He brings in a clerk from the purchasing department to help the two regular assistants. Even with this extra help they have to work until 9 or 10 at night to get the schedule done. Also no one has Harry's skill in handling the morning's traffic emergencies. During Harry's holidays the drivers tolerate this chaos because they know it is only temporary.

It is obvious that Harry is a rare sort of person and any assistant must have like characteristics. He must provide instructions so that the lorries can be loaded up efficiently by the night shift. Each lorry must contain a package of orders to different customers and in delivering these orders each driver must be given a fair day's work. The driver must be advised on the best route to deliver his orders. If the driver runs into unexpected difficulties someone must be able to help him complete his deliveries. It is difficult to find people with the ability to make these complicated decisions speedily, efficiently and over a long working day. Of Harry's present assistants, Mrs Watkins is certainly the best; but she has three school-age children under twelve and cannot work overtime. Ray Price, aged twenty, was attracted into the job by the good pay, over

50 per cent more than he could earn elsewhere. But he is getting fed up with the amount of overtime he has to do. Harry has had four such assistants in the last five years, all of whom left because of the strain of the work.

Ever since the unsuccessful attempts to computerise the despatch department's work, Harry has been suspicious of change and rather evasive in explaining to outsiders how his 'system' works.

Initial Exercise in Diagnostics

Read the case and *immediately after* give your gut reaction to the statements below, using the following scheme:
  √ I agree with this statement
  X I disagree with this statement
  ? I am unsure

34 opinions about the Harry Britton case:

1 It is a waste of Harry's skills to do routine jobs.
2 Conversely, it is the routine that Harry loves.
3 Something should have been done before.
4 Who is Harry's boss? I must find out.
5 When we set out all the alternatives, don't forget the no-change option.
6 Deal with emergency orders separately.
7 It is the accounts department which really needs sorting out.
8 Computerise just the loading not the routing.
9 Computerise just the routing not the loading.
10 We need to find a new, younger and healthier Harry.
11 Drivers should do some of Harry's routine tasks.
12 Drivers could do some of Harry's routine tasks.
13 Drivers would do some of Harry's routine tasks.
14 Introduce shiftwork into the despatch department.
15 Give Price more money and more responsibility.
16 Get Harry to a doctor.
17 Get Harry to a psychiatrist.
18 Find out how similar firms manage.
19 Bring Miller over to work in despatch.
20 Hive off a lot of despatch's work to other departments.
21 Generous early retirement offer and consultant status for Harry.

22 Secretly, Harry likes all the fuss that is being made over him.
23 Mrs Watkins is a square peg in a round hole.
24 Give Harry a stake in the firm.
25 Run a computer-based system parallel to Harry's.
26 Get more office staff for Harry.
27 Jarvis would sort the whole thing out if you gave him a try.
28 NBD don't really need such high delivery standards.
29 Get a better system going quickly whatever the cost.
30 You're kidding. We've been asked to carry out a cost-cutting exercise.
31 How much time will any reorganisation take? I need to know.
32 Find out who is going to try to stop any reorganisation, apart from Harry.
33 It is important to do things in the right order.
34 But first find out the right things to do.

Follow-up Exercise in Implementation

The 34 statements were generated as a result of three parallel brainstorming sessions. Within these statements are some very good ideas (and some dud ones). Brainstorming is all very well for generating every possible approach but it needs to be followed up by a classifying and weeding-out process. Take the 34 ideas and slot them into the following classifications.

Classifications	*Insert 'ideas' 1–34*
(a) Establishing credibility as a *change agent*	
(b) Resolving difference of opinions over *objectives*	
(c) Establishing how any new despatch system is going to be *monitored* and *evaluated*	
(d) Obtaining the right level of resources for a despatching *strategy*	
(e) Spelling out, costing and sequencing the *plan* for a new despatching strategy	

(f)   Showing how despatch *tactics*
        should be delegated

(g)   Showing how people are going
        to *operate* the new despatch
        procedures

Some of your boxes will be overloaded with good ideas. Others will be nearly empty or contain unsatisfactory approaches. In the latter case, generate some more. As a rough guide, you will need to expand the 34 original ideas to 50+. If you, as a consultant, then attack the problem in the order (a), (b), (c) etc. you are on the way to getting a good result.

General Issues which the Harry Britton Case Raises

(1) Adjusting the nature of a job to changed circumstances   Once having given a worker tasks and a title it can be quite hard to shake off its traditional connotations at a later date. We may still think of 'butcher, baker and candlestick maker' even if they are 'deep-freeze salesman, sandwich-bar assistant and lampshade manufacturer'. All workers must be prepared to adapt to technical innovation whether it affects their job directly or indirectly, e.g. postmen to electronic mail, lathe operators to CNC machines, solicitors to computerised conveyancing. And Harry Britton must come to terms with the computer revolution. It helps if NBD shows that it is committed to using computers to *assist* Harry not to *replace* him.

(2) Identifying the beer-truck syndrome   This term comes from Gene Woolsey who describes a certain type of employee. 'If this person (and there is at least one in every absolutely crucial part of your business) should step off a curb and be struck by a speeding beer-truck, you have no backup who can do what he does. Further, as he does such a good job, the biggies of the corporation don't even know he is there and have even less under-standing of his importance.'

For example:

- the only man who knows the layout of the old sewers under the town hall (suppose his sport is hang-gliding);
- the part-time woman who is the only remaining member of the team of brilliant eggheads who run your idiosyncratic computerised stock-control system (suppose her husband has just been offered a job in Australia).

- the draughtsman who: knows that your most important customer is always a bit slapdash about filling in full details on the specification sheet; has a marvellous memory for what the customer really wants; and is always available if a machinist isn't quite clear what should be done (suppose he's working up to his last heart attack).

All of these jobs need identifying and an understudy trained — *before* nemesis.

Overriding the 'indispensable workaholic'   Like the beer-truck syndrome this concerns a 'key link' in the organisation — but there is a difference:

(i)   he is not necessarily competent;
(ii)   he has made himself *appear* indispensable, and much of his time is spent in maintaining that illusion.

Annex to Method Study: Therbligs

Frank Gilbreth invented these to give a comprehensive but simple classification of all the main motions of an industrial worker. For completeness, we include a few rarely used Therbligs and a few recent additions.

Hand operations at a stationary workplace:

Grasp
Release load — freeing hand from load
Position — aligning an object
Pre-position — rarely used now (see *Position* above)
Assemble
Disassemble
Use — handling a tool or machine
Hold — fixing material while working on it

Moving objects by hand:

Transport loaded — i.e. an arm movement
Transport empty — movement of empty hand

Mental activities:

Plan — thinking, deciding, comprehending
Search — sweep of eyes
Find — end of search
Select — choosing an item from a group
Inspect — viewing or feeling an object's quality

Delays:

> *Rest* − recovering from fatigue
> *Unavoidable delay* − a pause arising from the nature of the operation
> *Avoidable delay* − a pause through idleness or inefficiency

Body movements other than head/hand/arm:

> *Walk*
> *Bend*
> *Sit*   } all pretty obvious
> *Stand-up*
> *Kneel*

Further Reading

Standard Texts

Delmar (1985) Chapter 5.
Hunter (1983) Chapter 9.
Lewis (1981) Chapter 8.
Mayer (1975) Parts 8 and 9.
Stevenson (1986) Chapter 8.

Specialist Texts

Carson, G.B. (1958) *Production Handbook,* 2nd edn, Ronald, New York, Good
   section on how to generate Method Study questions.
Evans, F. (1980) *Applications of MTM,* MTM Associates. Very detailed standard
   text for practitioners.
Gomberg, W. (1955) *A Trade Union Analysis of Time Study,* Prentice Hall. The
   title could mislead you. It is in fact a well-researched book of value to
   unionists, management and academics.
Jones, R. and Lakin, C. (1978) *The Carpetmakers,* McGraw-Hill. One year in the
   life of a carpet factory on the way out. Gripping true story of insuperable
   management problems.
Lee, J.A. (1980) *The Gold and the Garbage in Management Theories and Prescrip-
   tions,* Ohio University Press. A scholarly debunking of received wisdom
   embracing everything from Taylor's Scientific Management to the modern
   Human Relations schools. The highlight is Wrege and Perroni's 'What really
   happened at Taylor's ingot loading experiments', from the discovered
   notebooks of the junior work-study officer who supervised the experiments
   on Taylor's behalf. Also the famous Hawthorne experiments come under
   critical scrutiny.

Taylor, F.W. (1972) *Scientific Management,* Greenwood Press (first published 1911). More than a historic curiosity. Taylor's energy, obsession with detail, and forcefulness set new standards for generations of works managers.

Case Studies

Constable and New (1976) Bridge Electric (B).
Meier (1982) Bednap and Quick-lube.
Nicholson (1978) Micronair (again!).
Schmenner (1986) Dayton; Knox.

Note: The quotation from Gene Woolsey on the beer-truck syndrome can be found in the US Journal, *Interfaces*, August 1980, p. 11.

Chapter 5

MATERIALS MANAGEMENT

Introduction

All types of operation need 'materials' in the widest sense of the word
– from ores for the bulk-chemical industry to electrical components for
car manufacturers, from finished products for retailers to paper for
financial-service industries, from surgical instruments for health services
to diesel for transport operations. Whatever the material, it has to be
selected, purchased, handled, housed and utilised.

Let us start with a simple material-requirement situation and consider
the implications. When you buy petrol for a car you have several decisions
to make:

(1) What grade (2*, 3* or 4*) do I need to do the job? Should it be
lead-free? In other words you are asking yourself: What is the material
specification?

(2) Where shall I purchase it? In other words: What alternative suppliers
are there? How do they compare? What benefits do they offer?
Expanding the analysis of benefits: forecourt-attendant service may
be useful if you have your best clothes on, but irrelevant at other times;
price may be your No. 1 priority – occasionally you make a 10p/gallon
saving by shopping around during a petrol price war; if your fuel
indicator shows empty you will worry less about price, more about
the location and opening hours of the garage.

(3) How will you finance the purchase? Again there may be several
alternatives – cash, credit card or company account.

The problem of how to *handle* and *house* the petrol has been solved for
you by standard petrol pumps and car fuel tanks. But even then you can
buy locking petrol caps to ensure security of your valuable material during

storage. The effective *utilisation* of your material depends on such things as the condition of your car engine, the tyre pressures, and good map reading to get from A to B by the most fuel-economic route. In other words, a good maintenance programme and good planning increases your petrol-utilisation efficiency. You can see that, for a simple requirement like petrol, if you analyse the situation you have a whole range of factors to consider. The same factors are true of any material requirement; what differs is the time scale. For example, the petrol you purchase will probably last a few days. When you run low, rarely more than half an hour needs to elapse between your awareness that you are running short and the purchase and first use of the petrol. If we consider the crude-oil requirements of a major oil refinery the time scale is a different order of magnitude.

Material Selection

Let us take up the first point from the introduction: what specification does the material have to meet?

We considered this briefly in Chapter 2 when we looked at Value Analysis. We looked at alternative materials for each component of a product. Before we can decide if a material is suitable for our needs we need to know its properties.

For example, if we are looking for a material to make an aircraft wing, we consider properties such as strength, density, resistance to sand and salt erosion, fatigue resistance and tolerance to presence of cracks. Some materials which have to meet very high use specifications can be very difficult to manufacture − for instance the exacting requirements for turbine vane materials make the manufacturing process increasingly difficult. In fact, a whole casting needs to be grown from a single crystal.

Not all materials are selected for their superior properties. Cost can be a critical factor in less exacting circumstances. Thus, stainless steel is a superior material for car exhausts but it is used only on expensive models, since car manufacturers feel that the added cost of making exhausts out of this material is not a sensible marketing move.

Material Purchasing

General Overview: A Purchasing Manager Meditates on his Job

These comments come from the purchasing manager of a large local authority.

> Everyone thinks they can buy. We all go shopping for items from light
> bulbs to motor cars. And so we all think we are experts. But when it

comes to commercial buying, that is different. Purchasing is a profession like any other. You need specialist skills and experience. You need to know how to draw up a contract, what to look out for in any supplier, and who is reliable. You need to ensure *continuity* of supply. It is no good buying potatoes from a wholesaler who decides to have the week off when the mood takes him.

Although we are experts in *buying*, we still need to consult *users* about their exact requirements. For example the type of pencils children of 5 use is different from those used by 16-year-old art students. It is the teachers who are the experts at knowing the exact sort of pencils that are needed. Our job is to go off and try to get them and negotiate the best deal.

Working for a local authority we are perhaps more open to scrutiny than some private-sector purchasers. We get offered everything from free drinks to Mediterranean holidays, but we daren't accept even a bottle of whisky at Christmas, and have to make reports on all the meals bought for us. Not only must it *be* above board it must be *seen* to be so. Because we are accountable to councillors and ratepayers, there is a lot of red tape.

Sometimes delivery can be a problem. For example, take the heating oil delivered to our offices, schools and residential-care centres. The storage tanks at these places are of different sizes, and so are the entrances for the delivery vehicles. The oil companies provide tankers of different sizes so we have a scheduling problem on our hands.

Routine Purchasing Operations

It is a prime function of purchasing to ensure that there is *no ambiguity* when an order is placed with a supplier. For the most important purchases, a legal contract will need to be drawn up. Even for the less important items, orders need to be written out clarifying:

(i)   specifications
(ii) quantity
(iii) price and payment terms
(iv) mode and date of delivery.

Where there are many subtle variations in the material or goods being ordered, it helps to accompany the purchase order with:

(i)   a sample of the material wanted;
(ii) a reference number from the supplier's catalogue;
(iii) reference to an industry-standard specification (e.g. a BSI number);
(iv) reference to chemical or physical properties;
(v)   (for components) a blueprint of what is needed;
(vi) reference to the treatments or processes the material is expected to pass through before delivery.

You have to be careful about referring to 'looser' specifications such as *brand names*. For example, if you were ordering soft drinks for your chain of food stores, you would not simply ask for so many crates of 'Coca Cola'. You would want to say which variant you needed — 'Diet, Old, New or Cherry Coke' — and also (as the quality of water can vary around a country) from which bottling plant you would like it sent.

Follow-up procedures after the purchase order has been placed

(1) Soon after the order has been placed, phone the supplier to confirm that the order has been received and accepted.
(2) Just before the order is to be dispatched, confirm with the supplier that the delivery will be as planned. For an important order with a long lead time, it is advisable to make several regular checks on the progress of the order.
(3) Arrange with whoever is to receive the incoming goods to tell you of their arrival.
(4) Initiate an emergency procedure if the goods don't arrive on time. This is discussed in more detail in the 'tactical purchasing' section.

Record keeping   If you have a comprehensive data base of suppliers and materials, indexed and cross-referenced, this eases the purchasing routine. Where you need to find a new supplier, it is useful to establish a *search procedure* which even quite junior clerical staff can manage. This involves working through such sources as Kelly's and Kompass directories, *Yellow Pages,* Chambers of Commerce, trade associations and business libraries. If more experienced staff are to be involved in the search, it is best for them to concentrate on salesmen, users, scientists and professional contacts.

Good record keeping can also help management evaluate existing suppliers to avoid the worst and to direct more work to the best. Although *decisions* on this issue are matters of purchasing tactics and strategy, *preparing information* for these decisions is a key activity of the routine purchasing function. But one difficulty is how to take the information that is known about a supplier and to filter and simplify this information so that it is understandable to those making tactical and strategic purchasing decisions. Formally, this has been attempted by *vendor-rating systems.*

For each existing supplier you calculate an overall rating devised from 'weights' you give to certain attributes you think important (e.g. price = 0.5, quality = 0.3, delivery = 0.2). An overall vendor rating is calculated by applying these weights to data extracted from the supplier's previous performance, and summing the results. E.g.:

$$\text{Price rating} = 0.5 \times \frac{\text{lowest quote}}{\text{this supplier's quote}} = \text{(say)}\ 0.5 \times \frac{(£40)}{(£45)} = 0.44$$

$$\text{Quality rating} = 0.3 \times \frac{\text{defect rate of best supplier}}{\text{defect rate of this supplier}} = 0.3 \times \frac{(0.02)}{(0.06)} = 0.1$$

$$\text{Delivery rating} = 0.2 \times \frac{\text{lead time of best supplier}}{\text{lead time for this supplier}} = 0.2 \times \frac{(14 \text{ days})}{(21 \text{ days})} = 0.13$$

Total vendor rating (best possible would be 1.00) $= 0.67$

A vendor-rating system should be used only as a very rough rule-of-thumb device. It can never capture the full complexity of a supply situation. This point is emphasised if you look at all the complexities of prices, quality or delivery which are covered later in this purchasing section.

Supplier-vulnerability indices A better monitoring of suppliers would be via information outside that directly associated with purchase orders:

- analysis of company accounts to pick out suppliers that might be having cash-flow problems;
- a check on supplier's labour relations to see whether a strike, or overtime ban, is in the offing;
- a check on whether there has been any management change or takeover that affects a supplier;
- a check on whether there has been any trouble at a *supplier's supplier* as this could work its way through to you.

All these checks involve quite a lot of clerical effort, but are well worth establishing as part of the essential routine of a good purchasing department.

Tactical Purchasing

What sort of events can disrupt the day-to-day routine of a purchasing department? Arguments over price and discounts, late deliveries and late changes in specifications. Suppliers have to be cajoled, threatened, tempted and stimulated; in response, suppliers will try to influence the purchaser. Such activities all fall under the heading of purchasing *tactics*. As a first step, the purchasing officer must obtain some idea of how far, and when, he or she is going to get involved in personal negotiations. There is a useful rule of thumb which is shown in Figure 5.1.

Negotiate with whom? Suppose that your purchasing situation falls within the bottom-right-hand box in Figure 5.1 (an important deal for both you and your supplier). So you negotiate. But the first thing you must establish is the *credentials* of the person you are dealing with. Many a person has thought he has finalised a deal only to find out that it has to be approved by a

The importance to the supplier
of this deal

	Minor	Major
Minor	Delegate, dispose of quickly	Impose your system (e.g. ask for tenders or quotes)
Major	You are vulnerable to being squeezed or neglected: always have an alternative supplier in reserve	*Negotiate:* haggle; bargain; spend a lot of time with this supplier

The importance to you, the purchasing officer, of this particular deal

Figure 5.1

higher department or committee, or even that the supplier has to confirm the position with *his* supplier before the deal can go ahead. When negotiating, it helps a purchaser (and vendor) to have these distinctions in mind.

When the purchaser approaches the supplier's sales staff, they might be constrained by:

- their production manager (a delivery has to fit in with *his* schedule);
- the chief accountant (who needs to agree to any special discount);
- the general manager (who might have a business arrangement with a firm that is a rival of yours).

It may be that these people have a direct influence on the deal that you are negotiating. Or the sales staff may say that, much as they would like to make concessions to you, people above them in the organisation would veto it. (This is a useful negotiating ploy for the sales staff whether or not it is true.)

Obtaining price discounts   These are available for nearly every purchasable commodity, especially for a business with 'clout' or influence. In particular the fortunes of the big retailing chains have been enhanced by the discounts they obtain when purchasing. In general, discounts can be classified as follows:

(i)   discounts associated with the terms of payment, because you are a high-reputation company with little chance of defaulting, or because you settle immediately, or within a week or month;

(ii)   trade discounts to franchisees, shops, wholesalers, subsidiaries or trade partners;

(iii)   quantity discounts for large or regular orders, for orders from single rather than multiple sources, or for large standardised packs or containers;

(iv)   quality discounts for a standard 'no frills, no service' product, or for 'seconds' or substandards' (the reverse *premium* applies where extra quality, service or guarantees are required);

(v)   discounts where advance warning is given of an order, or where there is not a fierce delivery date (and the reverse premiums apply for rush orders or queue jumping);

(vi)   seasonal discounts (for example getting road-salt or coal in summer, electricity at night).

Is forward buying a valid tactic?   Suppose that your raw material is subject to large price swings over the year − e.g. any food product (coffee, cocoa, sugar, grain) where supply is subject to harvest variations; or any raw material (metals, chemicals) where demand is subject to surges arising from war or capital investment. It is tempting for a purchasing officer to play the market by ordering large immediate deliveries when the price is due to rise, and running down buffer stocks when the price is due to fall. This is only valid if the purchasing officer's information is better than the market's.

If you are speculating in coffee, do you really know more about the harvest than the trader in Brazil?

If you are speculating in copper, do you really know more about whether the US government is going to build up its stockpile than a Washington lobbyist?

In the above circumstances, the answer is rarely 'Yes'. On the other hand the purchasing officer's company may be in a unique position to know more than the market, as when Coca Cola switched from using saccharin to aspartame as a sweetener. By keeping such a move secret, they cornered the future production of aspartame and made it difficult for their rival, Pepsi-Cola, to follow suit. This was a classic *tactic*. It secured a temporary one-off advantage that would not be repeated.

Apart from having superior information, firms may have other inbuilt advantages that open the doors to forward buying policy:

● they may have lower-cost storage facilities;
● their use of a product may be growing more rapidly than that of other firms − if over-ordering occurs, stock will run down more quickly.

But, to summarise, if a firm has neither superior information nor superior facilities, 'tactical' purchasing is equivalent to gambling − a long-run loser. Further discussion of this issue can be found in Chapter 8.

Handling unsatisfactory supply situations What tactics can be adopted when a supplier is not meeting promised deadlines or providing poor quality? Here are two examples:

Situation (1) Crisis at Waterman's Printers For several years you have relied upon a small printing firm, Waterman's, to supply the printed package for your product (model-aircraft assembly kits). The packaging is a key element in the marketing of your product as it outlines how the model aircraft can be constructed. The printing is in colour with much fine detail. One month ago, for the first time that you can remember, Waterman's let you down. They sent a batch of packets where so many were smudged or badly registered that you returned them asking for replacements. A new batch was promised two days later but in fact arrived a week late. Although these were better, there were still minor imperfections and smudgings that you did not expect from a firm of Waterman's standing. You decide to visit the firm. You discover that Waterman senior is in hospital with terminal cancer and that his 20-year-old son is trying to keep the business going. He has already had to dismiss two senior employees for persistent theft. He has tried and failed to find suitable replacements. In the meantime, his remaining staff are struggling. Usually, at this time of year you place large orders with Waterman's in anticipation of the Christmas season. What should you do now?

Situation (2) Designer Guttering You are a Lake District builder under contract to complete a block of time-share apartments by 30 September. Your client has specified the installation of special plastic gutters, manufactured only in Austria, which do not break or clog up under heavy snowfalls. These gutters can be obtained from Designer Guttering (DG), Croydon who are the sole importing agents. To complete the apartments you really need to start work on installing the guttering by 1 August. To safeguard yourself against any hold-ups, you arrange with DG for your gutterings to be delivered on the afternoon of Monday, 1 July. They don't arrive. When you phone DG's office late on Monday afternoon, there is no answer nor is there any reply Tuesday morning. Finally, you get through on Tuesday afternoon.

'Grasmere Contractors here. You were supposed to deliver us some gutters yesterday.'

'I'm sorry sir, there is only me in the office and I'm only a temp. I'll get them to phone you back about it.'

Nothing happens, so you phone again repeatedly on Wednesday morning. No answer. In the afternoon, you get through to a Mr Howard.

'Oh, my partner Mr Biggins is handling the matter urgently. There has been some delay. He'll phone you and explain about it.'

No phone call, and you can't get anyone all day Thursday. On Friday, you are told that both Mr Howard and Mr Biggins are out of the office all day.

On Monday, 8 July when nothing has happened you can only get through to the temp. Losing your temper, you say you want to know *today* when you are going to get your guttering. Later, she phones back saying that Mr Biggins has arranged a definite delivery for Monday, 15 July. It doesn't turn up and you can't get them on the phone. On the 16th you can only get through to a temporary secretary. Raising merry hell, you get the home phone numbers of Mr Howard and Mr Biggins. In the evening you finally get through to Mr Biggins who is very apologetic.

'We just had an amazing flood of orders to handle and there was this dock strike. I'll send it off tomorrow first thing. No problem.'

Next day, and the next, and the next, nothing arrives.

How to handle these situations The above examples have different symptoms and you must apply different, suitable remedies.

Situation (1) A catastrophe due to an unforeseen act of God. (Any genuine natural disaster would count here but not 'the computer broke down' – that is used by the incompetent as an all-purpose excuse to shelter behind.)

Remedy Where good suppliers get into unavoidable trouble, provide help, but be careful that it is the right sort of help. In Waterman's case for example, there would be no point in giving them more rush orders that would overload an already stressful situation. You could help Waterman's fill their vacancy, or 'lend' a member of staff to tide over a crisis.

Situation (2) Irretrievable incompetence. Usual warning signs are:

- paperwork in a complete muddle and orders getting lost;
- poor workmanship due to poor foremanship;
- a *recurring* shortage of staff, material or machines;
- '*mañana* management' – continually putting off till tomorrow and breaking promises.

Remedy *Don't* hang around. Don't try to reform the supplier. Don't bluff them with threats. Order elsewhere immediately, even if expensive. If you have a contract with the 'incompetent firm' sort out legal claims against them later.

Strategic Purchasing

What weight should you give to purchasing management? It varies according to raw material value compared with all other costs. Where *value added* during processing is very large, purchasing is less significant. An extreme example would be that of the paints bought by an artist which can be a small fraction of the value of his picture. At the other extreme, it is very easy to refine, shape and stamp gold bars, whereas the purchase price of gold is phenomenal. So in the latter case a gold merchant must devote the bulk of his resources to forecasting gold prices and, for every deal, must haggle over the price to several decimal places.

Purchasing's importance also depends on the firm's *product mix*, (i.e. the number of different lines it has on sale). A large delicatessen will have hundreds of products, and much time needs to be spent on routine purchasing duties (placing, chasing and receiving orders). Contrariwise, a butcher may purchase only a few lines (pig, sheep and cattle carcasses) from one or two sources (abattoirs or wholesale freezers), so that the time on routine paperwork will be quite small.

What are the alternative ways that you can organise the purchasing function? This depends both on the weighting you give to purchasing and to the special logistic nature of your business. For example, to take two extremes:

- In a Japanese car company, the purchasing department's role is influenced by the Just-In-Time philosophy: frequent, regular, small deliveries and long-term relationships with suppliers.
- An independent European oil refiner, on the other hand, will be looking for irregular bulk-tanker deliveries (up to 500,000 tonnes), using the spot market to choose whatever supplier happens to be offering the best bargain.

In the first case (Japanese JIT), much of the clerical and tactical duties will be dealt with automatically. Instead, the purchasing staff will be involved in collaborative ventures with suppliers, helping them to improve quality standards and to design new products. In the second case (European oil-refiner), there will be a centralised, top-management decision on each purchase, the purchasing staff's vital duties being to monitor the progress of the oil delivery and to make sure that there is no hitch on the way. The purchasing staff will not have a one-to-one personal relationship with a supplier. Both very different purchasing methods are suitable for their own particular situation.

Further purchasing alternatives concern the *span of processes* that your firm wishes to cover. Your firm may plan *backward integration* by buying up suppliers and this will obviously affect your attitude to them. In such circumstances it is desirable for a larger part of a supplier's business to be routed through your firm, making it more dependent. To achieve this, special deals or discounts may need to be offered to the supplier to entice him to deal exclusively with you. Obviously, this has to be initiated by top management even if implemented by the purchasing department. It is all part of the longer-term *make-or-buy* policy of a firm.

Alternatively, your firm may wish to concentrate its activities and cut out certain peripheral parts of its business. This can be done in two ways:

(1) Using more *subcontractors*. This involves having a larger purchasing department to deal with the extra subcontracting work, checking on their credentials, supply capabilities and costings.
(2) Setting up a previous department of the company as an *arm's-length subsidiary*. In this case the purchasing department will be given very strict rules, for legal and tax purposes, concerning the price at which materials must be bought from such subsidiaries.

The strength of the purchaser—supplier relationship The weakest association is where a supplier has to *tender or quote* for each new order regardless of its previous association with the buyer.

Next, there might be a *rough ranking* of suppliers. For example:

A Class Suppliers with the best record: to be given preference and the bulk of orders if the situation permits.
B Class Satisfactory suppliers: to be used if no A Class available.
C Class Unsatisfactory suppliers: to be used only in exceptional circumstances.

A stronger relationship exists where established suppliers are given *blanket orders* for some time into the future. To a certain extent the supplier delivers at his convenience. Such suppliers may also be the permanent holders of certain jigs, tools, moulds or testing equipment belonging to the purchaser. From here there is a natural extension for the purchaser to get more and more interested in the processes, control systems and inspection procedures of the supplier. This is the subject matter of *Quality Assurance*, discussed in Chapter 6.

Material Deliveries

In many industries the transport of material is a vital part of the business. Such transport has recently been transformed by certain significant improvements in the following areas.

Road Transport

A wide range of businesses have reorganised their transport system to take advantage of the standardised *container*. This has outside dimensions of 6m × 2.4m × 2.4m and space inside to carry about 25 cubic metres of freight. The container (or rather the axles of the lorry that carries it) is strong enough to take up to 20 tonnes in weight. Containers can be easily transferred between road, rail and sea transport, they stack easily and protect the material from damage or theft. Cargo in a properly sealed container can be accompanied by simple documents speeding up the work of handlers and customs men.

What has been the overall consequence of the container revolution? In the age before containers, *the load was modified or broken up to conform to the transport and handling facilities* (e.g. re-packaged or jiggled around to fit in with the different capacities of a lorry/train/ship/crane/warehouse-rack). Now, with the container unit as the universal load, *the transport and handling facilities are adjusted to conform to the container* (lorries, gantries or ships are *designed* so that their strength, performance and dimensions are tailored to the standard container).

Accompanying the container revolution has been the relaxation in the legal weight restriction for road transport. In particular there has been a move towards a 40-ft-long, up to 40-tonne, wheeled trailer which can be easily attached to the cab unit of the lorry that tows it. Such a trailer is not so sealed as a metal box container. Nevertheless, customs authorities will handle it speedily if it has been covered and secured up to a certain international standard: 'Transport International Routier'. Hence the name 'TIR-trailers' for such units.

Obviously TIR-trailers and containers are closely connected developments. In particular they offer:

(i)   security during transit
(ii)   standardised dimensions
(iii)   economies of scale

There are, however, certain differences:

(i)   trailers cannot be stacked
(ii)   trailers can hold a greater weight
(iii)   'articulated' trailers can be coupled and towed by one cab

As a result of these differences, a driver and cab is more likely to take a trailer from source to destination than a container.

Shipping

The road-transport container revolution has had two spin-off developments at sea.

Container ships   Holding between 2,000 and 4,000 containers in neatly boxed stacks, these do away with complicated storage of cargo in holds. Cranes installed on their decks can enable them to do their own loading and unloading, and to visit ports with limited handling facilities.

Ro-ro ferries Roll-on roll-off ferries have bows which can be lowered and used as a loading ramp. This enables lorries to drive on and off themselves without the need for lifting gear or dock labour, which speeds up transit over short sea crossings such as the English Channel.

Increased specialisation and scale of ships Another development in shipping, unrelated to the container revolution, has been the greater use of bulk carriers for ore, cement and fertilisers. Also in oil, very large 500,000-tonne supertankers are used on the long-haul routes from the Persian Gulf to Japan and Europe.

Although large specialist ships can cut direct transport costs (arising from fuel or labour) there are certain extra indirect costs:

(1) *Handling* Big ships need deeper water terminals and wider, more deeply dredged channels and canals.
(2) *Shore storage* Greater stocks of raw materials need to be held at both the loading and the unloading port, requiring the construction of more warehouses or storage tanks.
(3) *Accidents* Greater size increases the chance of certain sorts of accident. Gases that have accumulated in an empty oil tanker can blow it up. If it happens to be a berthed supertanker, it can blow up all the surrounding facilities as well (as at Bantry Bay). All bulk carriers take a long time to decelerate or change direction, thus increasing the danger of collision. Also bulk carriers have now reached such a size that they are subject to catastrophic design failures in storm conditions.
(4) *Over-capacity* If (as in oil) there is a downturn in trade, it is more difficult to scrap or adapt a fleet of unemployed large specialist carriers.

Air Freight

Compared with surface freight, air freight charges are complex, with many discounts or variations depending on the weight, volume, commodity, carrier or routes. In general, air-freight rates discriminate against *weight* rather than *volume*. Consequently, goods of quite low value can be sent by air if they are made of low-density material (e.g. plastics or clothes) or if there is a lot of air space in the packing (e.g. toys). The higher cost of air freight has led to agents offering *groupage* or *consolidation* services. Here, several customers share costs by packing their small loads into one air container. The main advantage of air travel − speed − has led to the rapid expansion of express delivery service, under 24 hours for example within many parts of the USA.

General Consequence of Freighting Improvements

Increasing use of door-to-door delivery services has led to the decline of traditional transhipment methods such as railway marshalling yards and conventional crane docks. Location of new factories and warehouses now pays more attention to access to the motorway network, airports and container ports. The availability of a cheaper, speedier and more regular freighting system has transformed certain industries. For example, hypermarket and supermarket chains depend on a daily distribution network to underpin their operations.

The Storage and Handling of Material

Principles of Storage

Different materials have different storage requirements. We can classify storage situations into three basic types:

(1) Where you must prevent a break-in (by fire, water or vermin, or theft). Here the cost spent on securing the material, plus the insurance, is fairly easy to calculate, potential loss being limited to the total value of the material.

(2) Where you must prevent the material breaking out of its containers (e.g. explosives, corrosives, poisons, radioactives). Here it is much harder to specify the money that should be spent on storage, handling and insurance. Potential damage is open-ended, possibly far in excess of the value of the material.

(3) Where special consideration must be given to the movement of items. For example:

- *fragile* items requiring special packaging (eggs, glass, pottery);
- *powdery* or *liquid* materials, sloppy but easy to pump (oil, grain);
- *heavy* items (steel or concrete sections, assembled units such as generating sets). In particular, where a mixture of heavy and light items is being carried, it is desirable to arrange a *balanced load.*

In stowing or storing a mixture of items, there are many other factors apart from weight which have to be taken into account. Cotton bales can suffer rust from a ship's sides. Damp wool is liable to spontaneous combustion. Vapours from copra would taint other cargo but it cannot be ventilated. Apples exude carbon dioxide and need to be wrapped in chemically treated paper. Many common commodities have specific and unusual physical properties which have a dramatic effect on how they are stored and handled. This requires managers responsible for loading and warehousing to be fully conversant with materials technology.

This needs to be emphasised as there has been a tendency to think of inventory management as being limited to certain decisions regarding re-ordering and batching policies discussed in Chapter 9.

Generating Principles for Evaluating Handling Methods

When looking at alternative handling methods what are the main points to bear in mind?

Basically the analysis should follow the recommended approach to evaluating a machine (Chapter 3). But care should be taken to cover these complications:

(1) If you are making a minor alteration to the system the new handling device will have to fit in with the throughputs before and after it. But if you are making a major change, the new handling system may set the pace for everything else. (See the comments on the container revolution earlier in this chapter.)

(2) For any proposed change, *all* new tasks and work practices must be included. There is often a hidden labour element. Large transporters may need a 'mate' for reversing and precise positioning. Supervisors may be needed at a critical connecting point between 'automatic' handling processes. Or the containers used in automatic handling may have to be stacked and returned manually when empty.

(3) Following from this, any new handling system should take account of the extra capital cost of all new containers needed, plus the extra storage cost if a greater volume of materials needs to be held. And extra space will be needed to accommodate such containers.

(4) An advanced system in terms of speed and cost can sometimes be less flexible. For example, suppose you move your heavy loads by a system of cranes running on overhead rails. Whatever other advantages such a system has, it forbids cranes from passing each other in opposite directions (and of course it debars any other use of the upper part of a building).

(5) A distinction should be made between general-purpose and bespoke handling systems. A bespoke system is unique, and will be installed by consultants or the firm's own industrial engineers. If the new handling system doesn't work, it will only have a scrap value. A general handling system (e.g. a fork-lift truck or all-purpose robot) can be used by others, and if it is unsuccessful it can be sold, at quite a high price.

Situation Study: Material Handling in a Coal Mine

Branching from a main 'roadway' are two 'side roads' which tunnel each side of a coal seam. Coal is excavated between the side roads as shown in Figure 5.2.

Constraints on handling building material for 'side road' construction:

(1) The material is bulky and difficult to manoeuvre in a confined space.
(2) It is difficult to avoid interference if you want to extract coal and build side roads simultaneously.
(3) Operations are affected by geological uncertainties. Will the seam get shallower or thicker? Will it rise or fall? Will it be wavy or straight?
(4) Communications will be imperfect because of the noise, heat and dust, and the isolation of work teams.
(5) Every mine will have a unique network of roadways leading to a face. Work will take place at different levels. Roadways will be diverted

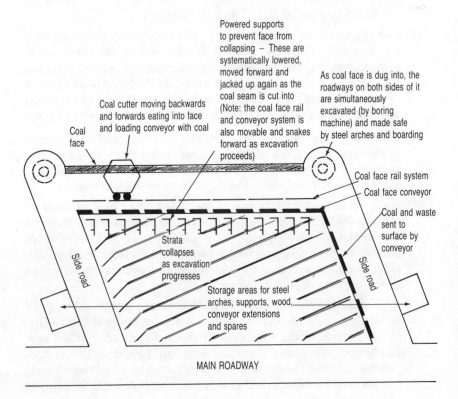

Figure 5.2   Material handling in a coal mine

to avoid or merge with roadways in neighbouring collieries. Movements in strata will cause roadways to twist and buckle.

(6) One pit will have several faces operating simultaneously, all competing for supplies of materials to be delivered to them.

Consequences of the constraints:

(1) From day to day there is an uneven pace of extraction, causing variable demand for building materials.

(2) It is difficult to forecast how far a face will advance before being abandoned. It could be 500m or 3,000m.

(3) Dispersal of faces means that different teams of men will be reponsible for passing on materials at different points in the system. Decisions will have to be made about which face is to have priority if there is a shortage of resources.

Lines on which any remedy must proceed:

(1) It is not feasible to set up independent material handling systems in the same pit (i.e. it wouldn't work to have independent arrangements for each coal face). You have to operate a global handling system for the pit covering all the constraints for every face. How should they interact? How, when and where should all material be moved? What resources are needed to achieve this?

(2) Any representation must be acceptable and understandable to the men underground who are taking and implementing the handling decisions.

(3) It helps if the decision maker has alternative proposals which can be easily compared and evaluated.

(4) The decision maker must *like* the proposed approach to solving the problem. The real test comes when the planner has left. Does the decision maker revert to old methods? Or does he update and improve the proposed method?

The Operational Research Executive Group of British Coal is developing HAULSTAR. This is a visual interactive colour simulation of material handling which is run from an IBM PC. Into the computer you input the materials requirement to achieve planned advances for all coal faces at a mine, and complete information about the network of mine roads and handling facilities. The program then generates the following information:

- identification of the transfer and storage points which may be potential bottlenecks;

- evaluation of alternative solutions, e.g. sending either individual small deliveries or bulk deliveries lasting several days to a coal face;

- variations and delays in material delivery caused by development work, coal extractions or the transport of men to and from the face.

For each alternative, the program visually displays or writes to file:

- the timing and quantity of material passing through intermediate points and reaching destinations;
- the location, movement and return of vehicles;
- the utilisation of the teams on each haulage route.

A decision maker can observe the flow of materials simulated for any particular solution, and can analyse variations quickly by changing the resources or relaxing/tightening constraints.

Exercise

1. Go to a supermarket at its busiest time and observe staff replenishing shelves.

   (a) What handling device do they use to transport the merchandise?
   (b) How much interference occurs between staff and shoppers?
   (c) Are goods being replaced when levels are low, or just when out of stock?
   (d) Are shelves being completely filled up, or spaces left?
   (e) Is the assistant doing the replenishment by zig-zagging about or following a logical route?
   (f) Is the replenishment done by an individual or in pairs?
   (g) When an assistant has finished a load, what sort of delay is there before he or she returns with a new load?
   (h) Are assistants looking for spaces on the shelves that they should fill, or are they following a predetermined system?
   (i) Is old stock being moved to the front of a shelf and new stock placed behind it?

2. Repeat the exercise for a hypermarket and compare. The results should be surprisingly different.

Minimising Material Wastage

So far we have looked at the activities of specialists who manage just a certain aspect of materials. Overall, the firm aims to knit together these activities to obtain effective materials utilisation. A trained eye can soon pick out firms which are good or bad at this. Bad firms tend to have:

- a traditional percentage loss that they tolerate through staff thefts;
- some very prosperous-looking scrap merchants as customers;
- large amounts of dead stock, rusting or mouldering in quiet corners.

There are several types of overall remedy that can be applied to a bad situation.

(1) A completely different operating system   In manufacturing, you can improve utilisation by capital investment on new and more efficient plant. Or, where there is minimum holding of work-in-progress, by adopting a *Just-In-Time* system.

But there are noticeable examples in other sectors. In finance and retailing, the more effective handling of transactions by plastic credit cards enables less stocks of cash to be held. And in distribution, the replacement of the glass bottle for milk and mineral-water delivery has led to the abandonment of the expensive cycle of returning empties.

(2) A redesigned product   Products are often over-engineered. Too much 'safety' is built into simple products, wasting valuable materials. Some companies have recognised this and redesigned products accordingly. For example, disposable razors do not need to last for ever, do not need to withstand great stresses and no longer need 'moving' parts. The blade has been reduced to about 25 per cent of the size of that in conventional razors and the rest of the razor is made totally of plastic since no screw is needed to hold the blade in. The later designs have even cut away sections from the handle to reduce material wastage further.

(3) Finer control of material processing   This is particularly relevant where material passes through a chain of processes. For example, in an oil refinery one has to be very wary of scheduling plants at the end of the refinery process at full capacity if, by doing so, plants that feed them are forced to flare their gas output or to send high-grade oil for fuel blending. Likewise in an integrated steelworks, one wishes to avoid rejecting an expensive finished product because of an error in the original casting. Commonly, there can be lack of co-ordination because effective processing of material today depends on the requisitioning and prior processing of other material several weeks earlier. This topic is considered in more detail in the sections on *material-requirement planning* and *project planning* (Chapters 9 and 10).

(4) Re-organised documentation and control   At-risk materials may be put in a special store with a storeman responsible for monitoring their use.

A common example is the tool crib in an engineering works. Machine operators will go to this crib to sign for any cutting tools that they need and must return them afterwards. Similar arrangements are found in hospitals to requisition instruments, in the services for ammunition, and in general where a business has a vehicle pool or stationery store.

(5) Tighter perimeter security   This aims to minimise material losses at the point where people leave the premises. For example, shops and libraries are cutting back on customer thefts by installing magnetic tags which activate an electronic alarm at the point of exit. Security fences likewise can have tripwires which trigger alarms. Where security men must vet people it is a good idea to do this scientifically by:

● randomising both whom will be searched and the intensity of search on any particular day (London Transport have achieved great success by having certain 'blitzkrieg' attacks on fare-dodgers);

● paying specific attention to certain subtly abnormal features (customs officers pay attention to a traveller with an unusually regular number of visits to a country, or one who has not stayed in a country long enough for a normal visit).

(6) Tighter internal supervision   This aims to put responsibility for high material utilisation on the first-line foreman or supervisors. An extreme example is provided by the Heron chain of garages. At any garage, if there is a discrepancy between the week's takings and the value of goods sold, the staff at that particular garage bear the loss themselves. This may appear harsh, but it is to a certain extent justified by a widespread human trait to pilfer if, *at the time*, one gets away with it. For example, the big breweries and the Post Office have very effective auditing systems for catching staff thefts months later. But sadly, there are still a number of pub managers and postmen who commit thefts (and invariably get caught). A system of near-instant control is needed to improve these situations.

A Cautionary Tale

A company producing plastic bags was very proud of its percentage utilisation of incoming material. It used high-grade plastic to produce high-quality plastic bags. Any wastage was recycled and included in the mix for lower-grade bags. Again, wastage from this process was used in the production of even-lower-grade bags, and so on. The percentage of wastage at any stage was not considered a problem, since it was being recycled. The company was fooling itself. Why?

CASE STUDY: COLEMANITE

To make glass you need three basic ingredients: boric oxide, calcium carbonate and silica.

Each of these compounds has interesting procurement problems. The most interesting is probably boric oxide, which the company can buy in two forms:

- as an expensive semi-processed chemical, which contains a *guaranteed* 57 per cent boric oxide;
- as a cheaper naturally occurring volcanic substance, colemanite, which contains a *variable* amount of boric oxide, on average about 42 per cent (colemanite is boric oxide mixed up with calcium, so some of the work that the glass furnace would normally do has already been done inside a volcano thousands of years ago).

The cheaper source looks the best but there are problems. The boric oxide concentration varies. Since this source is naturally occurring and dug out of a quarry, the boric oxide is associated with other undesirable materials, such as clay and felspar. These can be separated out by washing the ore but this is wasteful. The difficulty really starts with the location of the ore. The only place in which colemanite is found is in a particular region of Turkey. The initial selection of ore is crude and rather like selecting good bananas in a greengrocer's. The lumps of rock from the quarry are visually inspected and those which 'look right' are accepted and sent for washing, while the rest are rejected. This selection requires skill and experience. The company requires 3,000 tonnes per year of colemanite for its operation and this is equivalent to one full shipload per year. In other words, using this source, the technical manager needs to go out to Turkey once a year, choose visually a load which 'looks right' and ensure that he gets the selected load on to the ship for transportation to the UK.

After a two-week sea journey, the colemanite is shipped by road to be stored by a grinding company which supplies the glass company weekly with 60 tonnes of ground colemanite. As the year progresses, the boric oxide content in the weekly loads goes down due to settling of heavier materials. Therefore when a load arrives at the factory, it has to be tested for its boric oxide content.

Obtaining boric oxide from colemanite is very high risk and a bad batch can mean a very bad time for the company for a 12-month period. Colemanite may contain too much sodium and thus make the melt too alkaline, or a high percentage of calcium sulphate rather than borate. Nevertheless, despite all these problems, the company uses colemanite as its source. It does this because it has the skill to choose the right load and to utilise it effectively by adjusting furnace inputs to cope with varying percentages of boric oxide in the raw materials. At the end of the day, this gives better operating profits than taking the safe option.

Moral from the colemanite case   As well as knowing about the scientific properties of materials you need to knit in all aspects of:

- selection
- purchasing
- delivery
- storage
- handling
- inspection

Only with all these aspects covered will a materials policy be effective.

Further Reading

Standard Texts

Lockyer (1975) Chapter 18.
Lockyer (1986) Chapters 18, 29, 32.
Mayer (1975) Chapter 5.
Monks (1985) Chapter 5.

Specialist Texts

Lowe, D. (1973) *Transport and Delivery to EEC Customers,* Kogan Page. A very clear exposition of regulations, freight rates, frequencies, carriers and routes.

Case Studies

Meier (1982) Teem Aircraft Corporation.
Nicholson (1978) English Steel.
Schmenner (1986) Kalen's.

------ Chapter 6 ------

QUALITY

The Principles of Quality Assurance

Some large organisations need a very high standard of service from their suppliers. One way of achieving this is a 'prevention rather than cure' policy. The objective is to encourage a supplier to adopt good working practices in *every aspect* of his operating system, not just in the checks carried out before goods are passed on to the customers. Therefore, for example, to become an 'approved supplier' of the Ministry of Defence or Rolls Royce you have to let a representative of such organisations tour your factory and observe the skills of your workforce, the performance of your machinery and the co-ordination of your management. In the UK there has been a move to standardise what should be expected from a good supplier: in particular to compile a register of those firms that meet the principles laid down in British Standard 5750 specification.

Newcomers to quality assurance tend to find the BS 5750 guidelines rather unspecific. This is because the originators wanted their proposals to be applicable to a wide variety of industries and circumstances. To lay down absolute measurable criteria is often inappropriate. For example:

- You would expect a military rifle to need a higher specification than a fairground rifle.
- You would expect babyfood to have greater purity than petfood.

So, in laying down a quality system, you need to take account of the product or service being offered. It is for this reason that a quality-assurance inspector does not behave like a tyrannical sergeant major (i.e. does not walk around nit-picking and looking for trivial blemishes) but looks at the problems in context. In our experience he or she will be sympathetic to the special problems faced by the often small suppliers seeking admittance to the register. After a visit the inspector will offer constructive advice on remedial action. It is within this framework that the nineteen principles of BS 5750 summarised below should be viewed. They are subject to slight variations according to whether the operating system is *designing, manufacturing, inspecting, testing, installing,* or any combination of these.

(1) Quality's place in the firm's objectives Top management should have identified quality as a management priority and it should feature prominently in that firm's *corporate culture*.

(2) The status of quality assurance in the organisation In many organisations, one would expect someone to have the title 'quality-assurance manager'. He or she should have clear responsibilities and direct contact with top policy makers rather than being buried at the bottom of a firm's hierarchy.

(3) Performance evaluation of quality-assurance personnel A regular review should be carried out by top management to check on QA's effectiveness.

(4) Quality assurance's integration with other management departments This means establishing a satisfactory working relationship with accounting, marketing, production control, personnel, and R & D.

(5) Communicating customer requirements to the workforce Where the customer has submitted complex specifications, these should be translated so that the workforce find it easy to understand what is wanted.

(6) Keeping regular quality-assurance records These should be uncorruptible, accessible and understandable.

(7) Corrective action When faults are identified, an established procedure must exist for dealing with them.

(8) Design control Only peripheral to operations management, but set out at some length (11 subsections) for design firms.

(9) Control of documentation As well as having adequate documentation throughout the operating system, there should be a watchdog to check on whether any extra clerical system is being informally introduced, or whether any existing clerical system is being neglected.

(10) The standard of inspection equipment   This should be controlled, calibrated and maintained as per BS 5781 stipulations.

(11) A formalised purchasing system   The purchasing procedure should be written out and adhered to. You should expect a certain level of quality assurance from *your* suppliers.

(12) Manufacturing control   You must ensure that nothing has been omitted from the chain of manufacturing instructions and inspections. This is especially important for spot-welding or the detection of hairline cracks, where faults may be covered up by later finishing and assembly processes.

(13) Material quality   You must ensure that the quality of material does not deteriorate, and is not tampered with, from the moment it is delivered, through storage and handling, to its final incorporation in the product.

(14) Final inspection: special procedures   For some products this is the first chance to assess overall performance and the last chance to test before goods are sent to the customer. Where this is so, extensive testing should be carried out.

(15) Sampling procedures   These should be appropriate for the situation. The cost of inspection should be weighed against the cost of passing defective and rejecting acceptable goods. Causes and distribution of faults should be investigated and from this information a policy devised for the frequency of sampling. (See later in this chapter.)

(16) Non-conforming materials   There should be a policy laid down for handling 'substandards', 'reworks', 'returns', 'rejects' and 'scrap'.

(17) Knowing a material's inspection status   Whatever stage a material has reached in the operating system, everyone should know whether it:
- awaits inspection
- has been inspected and is OK
- has been inspected and rejected

(18) Material protection   Material should be guarded against theft, contamination, leakage, or knocks during handling.

(19) Training staff in quality assurance   This should include a record of the instructions given, courses attended and qualifications obtained.

You can see that BS 5750 has dragged quality assurance into the centre stage of operations management. It is no longer acceptable to limit maintenance of quality to testing and inspection stations on the sidelines of the operating processes.

QA Implementation

This illustration tries to capture the progress of a QA project carried out over a 6-month period. The company involved is an industry leader both in market share and quality. Previously quality was achieved informally. Then the firm's customers insisted that quality be demonstrated by gaining BS 5750 acceptance. Here are the notes of the project leader appointed to achieve this.

15 Nov. My project is to gain BS 5750 approval for the company's quality control system. For a start, for each item, there must be:

(1) a drawing or, if the part is to be bought in, a purchase record card;

(2) a process planning sheet, which lists the operations performed in manufacturing the item;

(3) a list of the gauges used to confirm that the item complies with the specified dimensions.

Each batch of items must have a batch card giving its material specification, description and code. This card serves as a record of the operations so far performed and the inspections made.

22 Nov. I've been looking at the systems in detail in the last week. I've got problems.

(1) Technical system. This system seems OK but the records are incomplete and out of date.

(2) Production-engineering system. A process planning sheet system does exist, but I haven't seen it used. People tend to do what they have always done.

(3) Production-control system. Batch records, route cards, departmental procedures exist, but don't seem to be followed. There seems to be a feeling that the priority is getting the work done, not sticking to the system.

(4) Inspection systems. These include calibration and sampling. A system exists but it is difficult to follow and so is largely ignored.

(5) Purchasing and sales systems. These seem to be OK but need to be brought up to date.

13 Dec. This is the progress I have made.

(1) The production planning sheets and drawings have now been revised, or drawn up from scratch if necessary.

(2)   All items are now issued with a batch card.

(3)   Bin cards have also been issued for all finished products.

(4)   A test and measuring check list has been drawing up showing calibration dates for all gauges and micrometers.

(5)   The quality manual and quality procedures have been revised.

(6)   Non-conforming materials and internal audit reports have been introduced.

(7)   There are problems with the sampling plan, but we'll have to see how it goes.

The main problem is that the shop-floor operation of the documentation system is still breaking down. With full order books, people just don't see the need to fill in batch cards, when they can manage without them. I think we will have to do more to sell the system to *all* the employees, the managers as well as the shop-floor operatives.

17 Jan.   A consultant visited last week and highlighted a number of non-compliances, but he felt we could be ready for assessment by the beginning of March. We decided to be on the safe side, and make it April.

The major problem seems to be gauges and their control and calibration. We will probably need to install a gauge store, but we've got nowhere to put it since the area I have in mind is needed for assembly work.

10 Feb.   Gauge records are still a headache. We've got cabinets and bins now, in which to keep the gauges, but people still borrow gauges and don't return them.

We've started a campaign to explain to staff why we are doing all this via departmental briefings. The message slowly seems to be getting through.

A few problems and shortcomings still exist in some systems but these don't seem insurmountable. The main thing is to get systems going but to keep the paperwork down to a minimum. We are carrying on with internal audits and failings are being remedied as we go along.

17 Mar.   I've started explaining to each employee *individually* exactly what quality procedures affect them. I make sure they each understand what is needed and why.

4 Apr.   BSI inspector visited us today and we've got a qualified pass. In other words we meet BS 5750 at last! (Just the odd thing to tidy up.)

The above illustration is typical of the normal problems encountered on the way to BS 5750 approval. There will always be a few frustrations, ups and downs and hold-ups. This particular project went well because the project leader was conscientious and was recognised as such by the

employees, and because management had a sincere desire to improve
quality.

Material Inspection and Quality Control

Introduction

In the world at large, material may be inspected for many reasons, for
example to further scientific knowledge. Not so in operations management. Here, inspection must have a direct economic purpose. Inspection
of materials is necessary:

 (i)   to decide what to do next with the material;
 (ii)   to identify a faulty previous process so that it can be corrected;
 (iii) to achieve the requirements of the ultimate consumer.

Again 'material' is used in the widest possible sense. Inspection procedures
originated in manufacturing industry but are applicable to a wide range
of businesses in services, retailing and distribution. For example, selection
of students for university places requires an inspection process. Whatever
the application, there are certain fundamental components to an inspection
system:

 (i)   how items are measured;
 (ii)   how inspection errors are classified;
 (iii) how the consequence of an inspection (or absence of one) is
        costed;
 (iv)   scientific method in laying out a full inspection process;
 (v)   diagnostics.

Attribute or Measurement Inspection

Inspection techniques vary according to whether the material is assessed
crudely by attribute or more numerically by interval measurement such
as length or weight.

Attribute inspection By this, we mean sorting material into just a few
major nominal categories often associated with properties relevant to the
consumer. E.g.

 bananas may be *unripe, saleable* or *over-ripe*
 body tissue may be *cancerous* or *normal*
 cheques may be *transactionable* or *invalid*
 legal defendants may be found *guilty* or *not guilty*
 water may be *drinkable* or *polluted*

Measurement inspection This is where an interval or ratio scale is used, often in fine detail. E.g.

weight of packaged food to the nearest hundredth of a gramme
dimensions of a screw to the nearest thousandth of an inch
constituents of an alloy in parts per million

These measurements may be needed *both* to aid the common attribute decision of 'ACCEPT/REJECT' for the consumer *and* to monitor and maintain quality during operations within a business. However, whatever the method of inspection:

(i)   it has to be cost-related;
(ii)   it has to be an integral part of other processes and should not be treated as an isolated activity;
(iii)   it has to be understandable to a wide range of employees and not just to certain specialists.

It is with these points in mind that we study inspection via a series of graded experiments.

The Matchbox Experiments

Equipment needed   Twenty boxes of matches. One sharp knife. Four coloured pens. A blindfold.

Preparations   You are going to make four types of **bad** match.

Dead   Take two boxes of matches. Light each match and *immediately* blow it out.

Short   Take another two boxes of matches. With the sharp knife cut off about one-tenth of an inch (or 2mm) from the non-striking end of each match. You needn't be too precise in the amount you cut off.

Bent   Take another two boxes of matches. Bend each match carefully until it splinters, but does not break in half. Then straighten the match out again.

Thin   Take another two boxes of matches. With the sharp knife, peel (very thin) shavings from the centre section of each match so that it is more round than square.

In later experiments all these matches are going to be mixed up and re-sorted. To speed up the identification process, it helps if you use a different colour pen to mark each of the four types of bad match.

Group the matches in piles of 100. In each pile put:

10 dead
10 short
10 bent   } collectively known as **bad** matches
10 thin

+60 **good** matches that you have not tampered with.

The proportion of bad to good in this exercise is clearly much, much higher than would be acceptable in real situations. This has been done deliberately to bring out the points we want to make more clearly and to make the exercise less time consuming.

With twenty boxes of matches you should be able to make at least seven piles of 100. Stir up each pile so that the good and bad are well mixed up.

Experiment 1: Evaluating a Single 'Blindfold' Inspection System

Many inspection systems are required to be speedy, cheap and minimise the labour element. As a result they sacrifice certainty. This experiment simulates such a 'blindfold' inspection system.

Sit in front of a pile of 100 matches and put on a blindfold. You are going to see if you can distinguish the good from the bad matches by feel alone. You may like to adopt your own way of doing this, but here is one suggestion.

Hold a normal, good match in your left hand so that the striking end of the match is near the tip of your index finger and the other end of the match is held by your thumb. With your right hand pick up a match from the pile. Compare the match's length by placing it next to the match held in the left hand. Whilst you are doing this, you will have to rely on the superficial feel of the match to decide whether it is dead, bent or thin. After this inspection, drop the match in **accept** or **reject** piles (making sure these piles can easily be located blindfold). For this first experiment, only have one reject pile (i.e. you don't have to specify which of the four types of bad match you think you are rejecting).

Inspect all 100 matches at a regular fast pace. You should *not* give yourself time to make too close an investigation of an individual match. You should maintain a speed of between 4 and 5 seconds per inspection cycle. Ideally, someone with a watch should monitor you to ensure that you keep to this pace.

An example of the pattern of results that you might achieve is shown in Figure 6.1.

Anyone watching the inspector at work is in a position to pick up interesting details, such as:

●   whether the inspector improves or deteriorates over time:

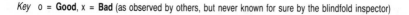

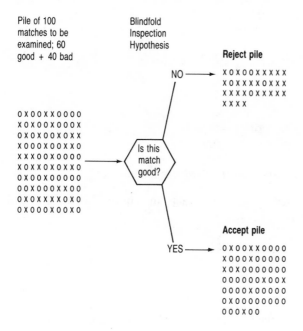

Figure 6.1

●   whether there is any particular type of match that is giving the inspector trouble.

But, for the purposes of the experiment, suppose that you don't tell the blindfold inspector everything that you observe about his performance. Suppose you don't give a running commentary on how he is doing, but merely tell him about his average performance when he has finished inspecting a pile. To wit:

How many good and bad matches are in his **accept** pile.
How many good and bad matches are in his **reject** pile.

From Figure 6.1 we can see that in our example:

    54 good matches were found in the **accept** pile
    12 bad matches were found in the **accept** pile
     6 good matches were found in the **reject** pile
    28 bad matches were found in the **reject** pile

Thus we can see that, of the 60 good matches fed into the system, 90 per cent were accepted and 10 per cent were rejected. Similar calculations can be done for the bad matches.

The inspector's performance can be portrayed as coefficients in a matrix.

$$\text{INPUTS} \quad \begin{array}{lcc} \textbf{Good} & \rightarrow .9 & .1 \\ & & \\ \textbf{Bad} & \rightarrow .3 & .7 \\ & \downarrow & \downarrow \\ & \textbf{Accept} & \textbf{Reject} \\ & \textbf{pile} & \textbf{pile} \end{array}$$

This is known as an *inspection transformation matrix*.

The inputs are multiplied by the coefficients and summed vertically to find the **accepts** or **rejects**.

e.g. 60 **good** $0.9 \times 60 = 54$ $0.1 \times 60 = 6$
    40 **bad** $0.3 \times 40 = 12$ $0.7 \times 40 = 28$
                                 66 accepts   34 rejects

If you feed in any other quantities of good and bad, the coefficients can be applied to work out acceptances and rejects.

Two of the above coefficients have special labels:

(i)   the 0.1 (the proportion of good matches sent to rejects) is associated with a *Type I* error, rejecting the true hypothesis 'This match is OK'.

(ii)   the 0.3 (the proportion of bad matches sent to accepts) is associated with a *Type II* error, accepting the false hypothesis 'This match is OK'.

To check that you understand the explanation so far, calculate the coefficients from the results of your experiment.

Evaluating the inspection process No inspection process exists in an economic vacuum:

(1)   There will be certain costs associated with the process and certain values attached to the stream of material going into and coming out of it.

(2)   Even in the most elementary situation an inspection process won't exist on its own, it will be part of a system. For example if material is rejected, someone has to sort and handle the rejects.

(3)   Material that has been accepted will be passed on to someone else who may either use it or return it as unsatisfactory. These

subsequent handlings will have costs and revenues which it is necessary to know about.

Returning to Experiment 1, suppose that the original blindfold inspection process is part of the system shown in Figure 6.2, which includes an infallible visual reinspection of rejects and customer returns.

The total costs associated with Figure 6.2 are:

Input	−400
Blindfold inspection	−100
Consumer returns	−120
Visual reinspection	−230
	−850

The total revenues associated with Figure 6.2 are:

Thin	+ 60
Bent	+ 20
Dead	0
Short	+100
Good	+720
	+900

Net profit is therefore: +50

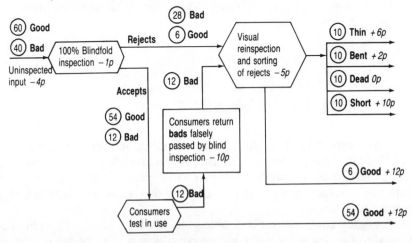

Figure 6.2

It is possible to obtain a neat shorthand representation of all the costs. First, trace each different type of item through the systems diagram, summing the costs.

Good matches accepted have costs of:

Input cost (4) + blindfold inspection (1)   = 5

Good matches rejected have costs of:

Input cost (4) + blindfold inspection (1) + visual
reinspection (5)   = 10

Bad matches accepted have costs of:

Input cost (4) + blindfold inspection (1) + consumer return
(10) + visual reinspection (5)   = 20

Bad matches rejected have costs of:

Input cost (4) + blindfold inspection (1) + visual
reinspection (5)   = 10

Put these costs per item in the right-hand part of each cell in the inspection transformation matrix.

Costs (pence per item) inset:

		TO	
		Accepts	**Rejects**
FROM	**Good**	5	10
	Bad	20	10

If you know the numbers going through the system, you can multiply them out by these costs to get total costs. Again, using the numbers illustrated in Figure 6.2:

		TO		
		Accepts	**Rejects**	
FROM	**Good**	54 × 5	6 × 10	= 850
	Bad	12 × 20	28 × 10	

If you repeat Experiment 1 with different volunteer inspectors, you will find that each produces a different inspection transformation matrix. Using these matrices and the costs given in Figure 6.2 you can see which inspector is achieving the best results. Note that we define 'best' entirely in monetary terms.

A quality controller must be able to justify the inspection system that he or she operates and must be able to put a money value on what is being done and the alternatives. This issue should take precedence over *all* other aspects of quality control, and yet is skimpily treated in the literature. In particular three questions must be answered:

(1)   What are the economic consequences of removing an inspection process from the system? Are we really much worse off?

(2)   What is so special about this particular inspection process? Aren't there many other alternatives, all giving about the same results?

(3)   What are the economic consequences of *adding* an inspection process to the existing system?

Let us take these three points and demonstrate what we mean.

(1) Removing an inspection process from the system   Refer to Figure 6.2. Suppose we had removed the blindfold inspection process (the cheap and quick inspection) and fed everything into visual reinspection (full infallible testing and sorting of all items), eliminating the need for customer returns. Figure 6.3 (overleaf) shows the new system.

Total revenue is +900 as before and total cost is −900, giving a net profit of 0. Any blindfold inspection process must be able to beat this or it is a non-starter.

(2) Do other alternatives give similar results?   Let us return to the inspection system which included the blindfold process. There is a spectrum of *very different* transformation matrices which give *very similar* economic results. For example, assuming we feed in 60 good matches and 40 bad matches as before:

This transformation
matrix . . .   with these flows . . .

				Accept	Reject
				50	50
Situation A	Accept	Reject			
Good	.67	.33	60 good →	40	20
Bad	.25	.75	40 bad →	10	30

. . . gives the same *economic* result (total cost 900, zero net profit) as this transformation
matrix . . .   with these flows . . .

				Accept	Reject
				35	65
Situation B	Accept	Reject			
Good	.50	.50	60 good →	30	30
Bad	.125	.875	40 bad →	5	35

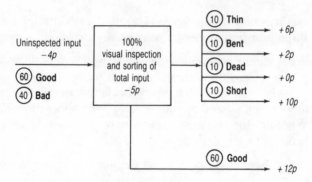

Figure 6.3

This can be confirmed by applying the relevant flows to the cost matrix:

Cost per unit	Accept	Reject
Good	5p	10p
Bad	20p	10p

The above two examples and all other solutions which give zero net profit can be charted as illustrated in Figure 6.4. The straight line formed by these points gives the boundary between worthwhile and unprofitable inspection systems. This clearly shows that an inspection system is worthwhile if the Type I and Type II error coefficients fall in the shaded area.

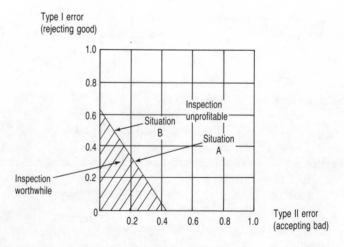

Figure 6.4 Breakeven chart for a blindfold inspection process which tests the hypothesis 'This is good'

However, if the range of alternatives merely trades off Type I for Type II errors (i.e. runs parallel to the boundary line), it doesn't matter which alternative you choose and a sophisticated evaluation of alternatives is a waste of effort.

(3) The economic consequence of adding extra inspection processes   This is best illustrated via an *exercise*.

Suppose you add a second blindfold inspection process as illustrated in Figure 6.5. Do your net profits go up or down if it costs 1p/item to operate? Use an inspection transformation matrix of $\begin{array}{|c|c|} \hline 0.9 & 0.1 \\ \hline 0.2 & 0.8 \\ \hline \end{array}$ to do your calculations.

Note that the second blindfold test could have been positioned to examine the reject rather than accept stream. It is left to the reader to check whether this is worthwhile.

In what industrial situations do you get *chains* of inspection process? If you get a chain of blind inspections on the *accepts*, this denotes a cautious but miserly approach. A bit like a hypochondriac seeking a second or third medical opinion from cheap but unconvincing doctors. A chain of blind inspectors on the *rejects* can indicate a quality controller more worried about short-run quantity targets than the longer-term effect of sending bad items to consumers, i.e following the motto 'Keep on testing and if I'm lucky enough to get an accept I'm in the clear to send it off.'

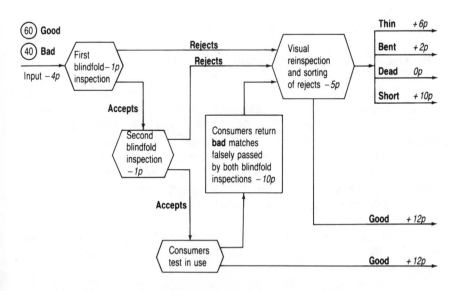

Figure 6.5

Example: Screening for Cervical Cancer

Sometimes we cannot cost our errors just in monetary terms. The effect of Type II errors in some situations is much more severe. For example, consider tests for cervical cancer. Recently in the UK it was found that on a second inspection of 45,000 tests (accepted initially as showing no abnormalities) 911 were found to show problems. At this point further testing took place on those 911 and 424 were cleared. Of the 487 women whose tests were still showing abnormalities, 157 needed to undergo various treatments to deal with cancerous growths. That is, there were 157 Type II errors.

The inspection process is clearly imperfect for several reasons. First, it is difficult to identify abnormal cells. At present it is matter of judgement not measurement. Second, the slide under inspection contains a sample of the smear taken, which in itself is a sample of the millions of cells in the area in which the cancer can attack. With these problems, it is unlikely that the test will ever be foolproof but crosschecking is obviously necessary and is being adopted to reduce errors.

We have so far looked only at the Type II errors in this example, but Type I errors also occur. Our best knowledge tells us that if 157 of the 911 needed treatment, then 754 were *probably* wrongly diagnosed and were in our terms Type I errors in the second inspection process. The worry caused by the woman thinking she may have cancer whilst she awaits the results of further tests is considerable. Naturally her faith in medical diagnostics will have been shaken. In equity, the further tests must be of higher standard.

The Use of Sampling in Quality Control

Our last example introduced the concept of sampling because 100 per cent visual inspection of millions of cells is clearly totally impossible. Sampling is used in many situations where the cost of inspection is high and/or the proportion of defectives is low. On the evidence of defects found in a sample a decision has to be made on whether to accept or reject the batch from which it was drawn. Before such a decision is made, statisticians find out about the quality standards expected in the specific business situation. There are certain standard definitions used:

Acceptance quality level (AQL)   If you examined output as a whole and found less than a certain percentage of defects, the AQL, the output would be acceptable.

Rejectable quality level (RQL) or lot tolerance percent defect (LTPD)   If you examined output as whole and found more than a certain percentage of defects, the RQL, the output would be rejected.

There may be a gap between the AQL and the RQL, indicating a quality level that you may be unhappy about but don't immediately reject.

Experiment 2

This takes up and develops the concepts introduced above. Let us assume an AQL of 11 per cent and an RQL of 28 per cent. Arrange for a blindfold inspector to test matches until he has generated (what he thinks are) 100 'accepts'. These should be placed in a bag so that no one can see if they are really good or bad. The blindfold inspector passes the bag to another person who accepts or rejects the whole bag after *visual inspection* of a random sample of ten matches that he withdraws from the bag. Suppose this person makes a snap judgement and comes up with these rules of thumb:

- **accept** if there are one or less defects in the sample of ten;
- **reject** if there are three or more defects in the sample of ten;
- otherwise, **sample another ten**.

The 1/10 and 3/10 sample decision points roughly correspond to the 11 per cent AQL and 28 per cent RQL. Later, we discuss why this relationship need not be precise.

Exercise Break   It would be a good idea to run through the experiment up to this point, getting another blindfold inspector to generate another bag of 100 of his 'accepts' and comparing the sampling results with the first run-through.

If you judged many bags of 100 in the above way, a pattern would emerge. On the whole, justice would be done.

If the sample found 3/10 or more matches to be bad, then this would usually correctly indicate a bad bag, containing 28/100 or more bad matches.

Similarly, if the sample found 1/10 or fewer matches to be bad, then this would usually correctly indicate a good bag, containing in total 11/100 or fewer bad matches.

Occasionally, though, your sample will give you a misleading impression of the whole bag. When this happens, you experience either a Type I error (rejecting a bag you should have taken), or a Type II error (accepting a bag you should have left).

In the particular jargon of acceptance sampling, a Type I error from sampling is known as *producer's risk* and a Type II error from sampling is known as *consumer's risk*.

The relationship between these errors, the rule-of-thumb sampling-decision rules, and the AQL and RQL can all be portrayed on an *operating characteristic (OC) curve*, as shown in Figure 6.6.

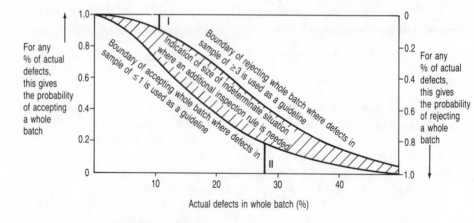

For any % of actual defects, this gives the probability of accepting a whole batch

For any % of actual defects, this gives the probability of rejecting a whole batch

Actual defects in whole batch (%)

What happens if a whole batch turns up with a (then unknown) percentage of defects just at the AQL level of, say, 11%? **Line I** tells you how frequently such a batch will be immediately rejected.

What happens if a whole batch turns up with a (then unknown) percentage of defects just at the RQL level of, say, 28%? **Line II** tells you how frequently such a batch will be immediately accepted.

I and II can be looked upon as 'What if?' producer and consumer risks. They are not *actual* producer and consumer risks, which depend on the distribution of defects in all the batches that arrive.

Figure 6.6 Operating characteristics curve for a sample of ten items using defect-in-sample levels of 1 and 3 as accept/reject guidelines

A Word of Warning

The decision-making capability of the OC curve and its constituents is often overstated. For example, it is often said that: 'A supplier and purchaser negotiate to arrive at mutually agreed levels of producer and consumer risks. These risks, together with the known AQL and RQL, can be analysed via OC curves to determine an optimal sampling policy.'

In our experience this conforms neither to business practice nor to logic. Producer and consumer risks, and AQLs and RQLs fluctuate according to the business environment, and the mix of suppliers and distribution outlets to which they are exposed. For example it may be necessary to take material from a less reliable supplier because the usual supplier has a strike on his hands. Or when breaking into a new market you may be sending material to first-time consumers who are going to have difficulty using it properly. Both these examples illustrate changes in the risk element. A proper response to such situations therefore is to apply a 'What if' approach via the operating characteristics curve, and to find out the consequences of various changes to:

(i)   the size of the sample;

(ii) the accept/reject guidelines (acceptance numbers) used with the sample.

But, to repeat, OC curves do *not* provide a comprehensive answer to a quality-control situation.

Quality Control with Irregular Quality of Inputs

The statistical control methods we have talked about are valid only if the inspection process has just one set of transformation coefficients *whatever the quality of input*. This is clearly not always the case. For example, when a doctor inspects patients, his success rate in diagnosis depends on the types of patient he has dealt with previously, e.g. a doctor returning from the tropics to Britain will be more likely to identify that a patient's fever is in fact malaria. Or, when a bon viveur attends a wine tasting, his ranking of the wines often depends on the *order* in which he has drunk them. Or, tell a teacher he is marking exam papers from an above-average class, and his marks may be different than if you hadn't told him this. Even pure machine inspections can be capricious. They can vary in efficiency according to age (spring weighing machine), throughput (volume meters) or type of input (coin phone boxes).

Consider this example which, for a while, baffled quality-control staff in a processed-food factory. Tins were being machine inspected on a fast-moving conveyor line. If a tin's seal was defective, a mechanical arm (the equivalent of a blind inspector) shoved the tin off the line into a reject basket. The inspection process was so fast and obscured by other machinery that it was difficult to observe what was going on. When baskets of rejects were removed from the conveyor area and examined carefully, the *proportion* of good/bad tins in the reject basket stayed at 50:50 regardless of the varying quality of the input, i.e. you got matrices like those shown in Figure 6.7 (a) and (b) for the same inspection process.

The answer was found when a videorecording was made of the inspection process and played back in slow motion. When the mechanical arm knocked a defective tin off the conveyor, its timing was slightly wrong and it was *knocking off the subsequent tin as well*.

Adaptive Quality Control

A system developed to inspect materials in which approximately 2/100 are defective will be inappropriate if the defect level rises to 10/100. In many processes such fluctuations can occur and methods to deal with them have been developed. These are known as *adaptive quality-control methods*.

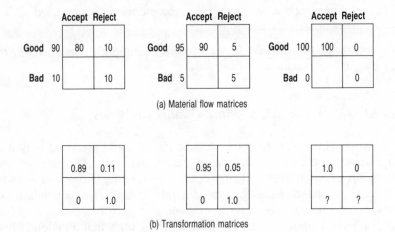

(a) Material flow matrices

(b) Transformation matrices

Figure 6.7

Adaptive quality control tries to walk a tightrope between:

- an expensive 100 per cent inspection, unnecessary if there is a long period of high quality; and
- limited sampling systems which, by themselves, cannot handle sudden ebbs and flows in the rate of defectives.

The advantage of adaptive quality-control procedures is demonstrated in the following experiments.

Experiment 3

This experiment has been designed to:

- give the reader a feel for the different intensity of quality control at different levels of alertness;
- show the necessary connections in a quality-control system which covers the full range of situations;
- illustrate a 'complex' system which is easy to evaluate and adjust — and understand;
- provide a format suitable for visual interactive modelling on a computer.

Take 500 matches including, as before, 60 per cent good and 10 per cent of each of the four bad types.

Part 1: Generating inputs of different quality   Select two volunteers: one to be a sorter, the other a quality controller (or inspector).

Randomly mix the matches and feed them in a long line to the sorter. The sorter examines the matches in sequence and puts them 50 to a box following these rules:

Rule 1   Initially, put only good matches into the box and put all bad matches aside. Then, when the sorter encounters three consecutive bad matches (of any type), he or she should put these aside. But *all* subsequent bad matches should be put in boxes (with the good matches) until another three consecutive bad matches are encountered.

These three should be put aside as should *all* subsequent BADs, as the sorter did initially. Later, when another three consecutive BADs are encountered, the sorter should switch again and so on.

This will lead to a swing backwards and forwards in the number of bad matches in the boxes.

Rule 2   If the sorter encounters two consecutive bad matches of the same type, these two must be discarded and *all* subsequent bad matches with this particular defect (e.g. thin) put in the box with the good matches.

This procedure will lead to a permanent deterioration in quality which will be corrected only by the quality controller's intervention. His job is explained in Part 2 of the experiment. The procedure should continue until the quality controller asks for this procedure to be stopped and asks the sorter to put all bad matches of this type aside as before.

Part 2: Inspecting varying quality via an adaptive system   The sorter passes boxes of 50 matches to the quality controller. The quality controller's job is best explained by the decision flow chart shown in Figure 6.8. It is useful if there are spare helpers to keep a record of what is going on and to organise the flow of matches through the sorter and quality controller. Matches which have been finished with can be mixed up and recirculated.

Instructions to quality controller   Enter the system. Pick up the first box of matches you are to inspect. Answer the question in the decision frame (initially frame A). Exit to the next relevant decision frame, decided by the number of rejects (bad matches) you found in your sample. Pick up the next box of matches. Answer the question in the decision frame in which you find yourself. Exit as directed by the number of rejects . . . and so on, as shown in Figure 6.8.

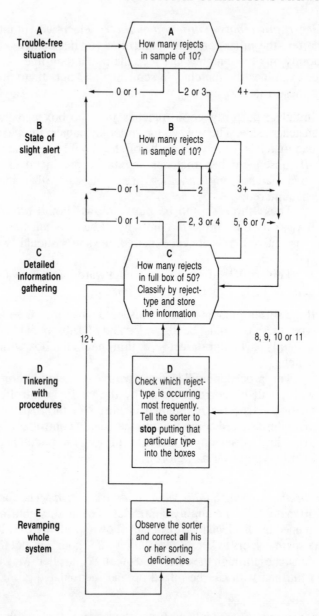

Figure 6.8 Decision flow chart

You can see that, as the level of rejects found in the samples goes up, we move from sampling 10/50 of the matches (the trouble-free system) to 100 per cent inspection. At a certain reject level the quality controller is in a state of slight alert ready to act should the reject situation deteriorate.

As the situation deteriorates, the controller starts collecting information to try to identify the problem causing the decreasing quality. As further deterioration takes places he or she begins tinkering with the procedures and finally, if this doesn't correct the problem, the whole system may need to be revamped. You can also see that when the situation improves the inspection *automatically* reverts to a 10/50 sampling system. Thus the system is adaptive to fluctuations in quality.

Review of the experiment   It is worth considering the following questions: How were the parameters of the quality controller's decision chart determined? Why are samples of 10 taken rather than 15 or 20? Why are '2 or 3 defects' in a sample rather than some other numbers used to move from a trouble-free situation to a state of slight alert?

When such adaptive systems are initially set up, the parameters are not determined precisely or mathematically — they are *ad hoc*, rule-of-thumb guesses. But after the system has been operating for a while, managers can observe whether it is biased towards the costly, high-quality *revamping* mode or towards the cheap, lower-quality *trouble-free sampling* mode. By a system of trial and error, better parameters can be adapted.

Employing Fine Measurements in Quality Control

So far, we have concentrated on the analysis of *attributes*, i.e. how to inspect material distinguished only by broad nominal classifications such as 'accept' or 'reject'. We now consider the consequences of inspection which employ measurements that can be counted, scaled and interpreted within the conventional mathematical number system, e.g. weights and dimensions. Before an inspection system based on measurement is constructed, three concepts must be specified:

  (i)   tolerance
  (ii)   precision
  (iii) accuracy.

Tolerance   This is determined usually by customer requirements but it is measured by the supplier's calibration equipment. For example, the specification of a product length may be $0.17 \pm 0.005''$. In terms of tolerance, this means that the tolerance *range* on the length of that product is $0.01''$.

Precision   It is important to distinguish between precision and accuracy. They depend partly on the skill of the operator, partly on how the machine has been set and partly on the machine's intrinsic performance capabilities. Rifle shots are *precise* if:

- they make small bullet holes in a target;
- on repetition, the shots are close together (see Figure 6.9a).

Accuracy Mortar guns are *accurate but not precise* if:

- a shot always covers the bull's-eye in a target but covers an awful lot of other space as well;
- different shots cover quite different areas (see Figure 6.9b).

Remembering these concepts, let us look at the results from a measurement inspection process. As we saw in our simulation Experiment 3, quality fluctuations are not always random — they are frequently caused by a problem or procedure. If we could identify these problems easily by inspection we could take corrective action, saving costly rejects being produced. The earlier that problems like this can be spotted the better. Clever measurement inspection may spot potential problems before the products begin to fall outside the tolerance range. Thus we can take corrective action even before rejects are produced.

Let us take the four sets of results A, B, C, and D shown in Figure 6.10. Deductions from the *pattern* of inspection measurements help us to identify the cause of problems.

When using patterns of measurement to investigate quality, a key feature is to establish *'How am I doing?' charts*, instantly recorded and visible to the operator and his or her mates at the workplace. The statistician is better employed in a background role, establishing what variations are

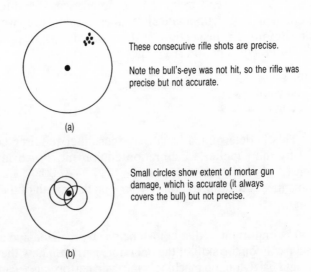

These consecutive rifle shots are precise.

Note the bull's-eye was not hit, so the rifle was precise but not accurate.

(a)

Small circles show extent of mortar gun damage, which is accurate (it always covers the bull) but not precise.

(b)

Figure 6.9

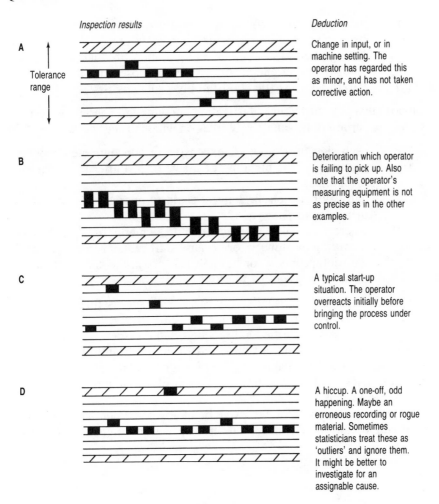

Figure 6.10

assignable to a cause (and therefore improvable) and what are due to limitations on measurement or machine setting. These latter random variations are known (rather misleadingly) as *process capability*. A full study of this topic takes us too deeply into statistics.

Diagnostics

The above example illustrates a proper use of statistics in quality control to indicate a worthwhile *direction* for exploration. There are other ways of finding useful direction indicators:

(i)   measuring new properties of materials;
(ii)   measuring at different points in the system;
(iii)   asking operators for their interpretation of what is going on;
(iv)   autopsy (experiencing the system by observing it);
(v)   Pareto analysis (tackling the big problems first).

Suppose that you start your investigation knowing little about the system.
There are certain rough-and-ready rules on where to start collecting data:

(i)   each side of a 'dodgy', expensive or subcontracted process;
(ii)   just prior to the blending of inputs or just after the separation
         of outputs;
(iii)   halfway between the longest chain of operations where infor-
         mation is missing;
(iv)   where incomplete or inaccurate data emerge because of faulty
         recording machinery, or because staff cannot record data or do
         their job properly, or because it is not in the nature of staff to
         do what is asked of them.

But remember, you can usually only carry out a successful investigation
with the co-operation of the operators or staff involved.

When you have identified a direction of attack to improve quality, it
is worthwhile constructing a Cause and Effect Diagram (also known as
a fishbone or Ishikawa diagram). The procedure is to start with the effect
and work backwards, constructing a branch-like system of causes which
could lead to that effect.

For example, consider excessive breakdown and poor-quality output
occurring on an office printer. The initial diagram might start like this.

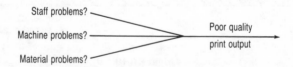

On exploring backwards through the question marks, possible major
causes are drawn as branches and minor (or secondary) causes as twigs
leading into those branches, as shown in Figure 6.11.

Having constructed quite a complex diagram like Figure 6.11, a most
likely chain of cause and effect is investigated working backwards from
the trunk towards a twig. As the investigation proceeds, dead ends are
encountered, or new information is gathered causing extra branches and
twigs to be drawn in. Often, the investigation has to backtrack towards
the trunk and set off in a new most-preferred direction. When a promising
twig is being investigated as a possible cause, all attention is focused on
it until a definite conclusion is reached. This involves:

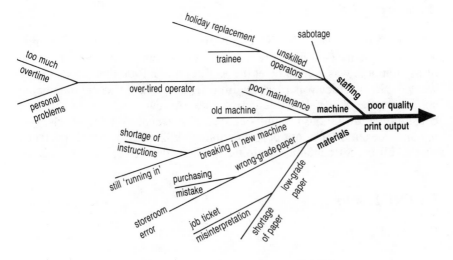

Figure 6.11   Cause and Effect Diagram

(i)   posing a hypothesis as to the cause of a fault;
(ii)   designing an experiment which is capable of confirming or rejecting the hypothesis;
(iii) acting on the results of the experiment to change operating procedures;
(iv)   confirming the improvement resulting from the changes.

Summing up Material Inspection and Quality Control

It is not enough for the methods of analysis to be statistically proficient. The prime aim of a quality-control system is to improve a company's profitability. With this objective uppermost, quality-control systems should aim to be:

(i)   cost and revenue conscious, including wherever possible costs of inspection and of outcomes rather than minimising or maximising other criteria;
(ii)   aware of the implications that one part of the system has on another — this includes, on the one hand, designing quality output with the ultimate consumer's criteria in mind and, on the other hand, exploring quality input back through a long chain of causes to identify areas of improvement;
(iii) a *manageable* management tool — this means being robust, flexible, and understandable.

A Japanese Tale

For a long time a large British engineering company had been unhappy about the quality of a high-grade alloy component supplied to it. None of its suppliers was able to meet the RQL of 8 per 1000 that the company wanted. So an order was placed with a Japanese firm, acceptance being subject to the 8 per 1000 defective rate. A few weeks later the first consignment of a thousand units arrived from Japan in two parcels, one big and one small. The big parcel contained 992 units, marked 'perfect'. The small parcel contained 8 units, marked 'defective, as requested'!

Further Reading

Standard Texts

Adam and Ebert (1986) Chapter 17.
Harding (1984) Chapter XVIII.
Lewis (1981) Chapter 22.
Schmenner (1987) Chapter 6.

Specialist Texts

Juran, J.M. and Gryna, F.M. (1970) *Quality Planning and Analysis,* McGraw-Hill. Comprehensive text for quality specialists, but very readable.

Case Studies

Constable and New (1976) Winton Shirt Company.
Meier (1982) Ohio.
Schmenner (1986) The problem with Kathy (A) and (B); Drug Distribution at Victoria Hospital.

Chapter 7

SYSTEMS

Systems Classifications

Q. Why do we want to classify systems?

A. (1) To help understand better what is going on.
   (2) To identify potential problems.
   (3) To improve the operation of the system.

Any representation of a system should aim to give balanced coverage to these aspects, illustrated in Figure 7.1:

   (1) What are the resources?
   (2) What are the transformation processes?
   (3) What is being transformed?
   (4) What is the desired end result?

   It is quite hard to achieve such a balance. Major business areas have their own 'natural' classifications which have a strong bias towards one of the above four aspects, as shown in Figure 7.2.

Designing the Appropriate Classification System

If these classifications are *just part* of an overall systems analysis there is nothing wrong in using them. The danger arises if one of the classifications is used as a major heading under which firms are assumed to have common problems. Things are rarely that simple.

(1) The problem of size Take *retailing* − logistics of Sainsbury's are clearly different from those of the corner shop.

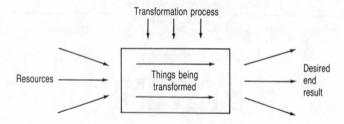

Figure 7.1

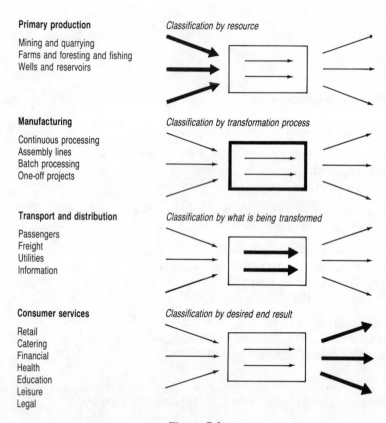

Primary production

Mining and quarrying
Farms and foresting and fishing
Wells and reservoirs

Classification by resource

Manufacturing

Continuous processing
Assembly lines
Batch processing
One-off projects

Classification by transformation process

Transport and distribution

Passengers
Freight
Utilities
Information

Classification by what is being transformed

Consumer services

Retail
Catering
Financial
Health
Education
Leisure
Legal

Classification by desired end result

Figure 7.2

(2) *The rarity of a pure classification* From *manufacturing,* take a bakery as an example. There are *continuous* ovens for baking standard loaves, *assembly lines* for confectionery and *batch* purchase and delivery systems. Most manufacturing firms, even quite small ones, will be found to have such a mixture of processes. Likewise in other sectors: airlines take

passengers and freight; a utility distribution company such as an Electricity Board also retails domestic appliances; solicitors provide legal and financial services.

Patterns of Transformation within a System

Take a closer look at an operating system and you will see a complex interaction between people, machinery, processes and materials. However, certain common strands emerge for a wide variety of systems, such as a factory, a rail network or department store. Some of these traits are illustrated in Figure 7.3.

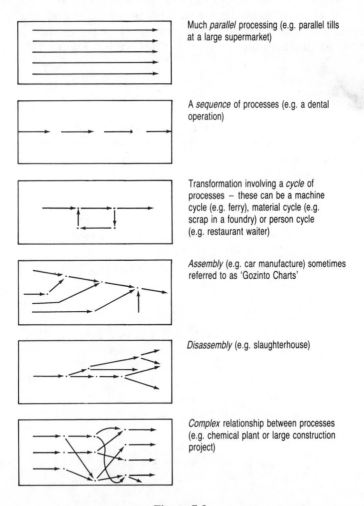

Much *parallel* processing (e.g. parallel tills at a large supermarket)

A *sequence* of processes (e.g. a dental operation)

Transformation involving a *cycle* of processes – these can be a machine cycle (e.g. ferry), material cycle (e.g. scrap in a foundry) or person cycle (e.g. restaurant waiter)

Assembly (e.g. car manufacture) sometimes referred to as 'Gozinto Charts'

Disassembly (e.g. slaughterhouse)

Complex relationship between processes (e.g. chemical plant or large construction project)

Figure 7.3

This is not an exhaustive list of patterns, but it covers enough of the common situations for you to identify the type of system which exists from observations of an operation.

Systems Diagrams

Segregating Inputs, Processes and Outputs

At whatever level a systems diagram is drawn, one would expect to see more complexity than arrows coming in and out of a box. An obvious extension is to split up processes into a sequence and also to note whereabouts in that sequence material enters or leaves the system. An example for the brewing industry is illustrated in Figure 7.4.

Scale Diagrams

Figure 7.4 is all very well, but it tells us nothing about the scale or layout of operations. So one improvement is to illustrate the operation via a three-dimensional diagram such as the one describing a hospital laundry system shown in Figure 7.5.

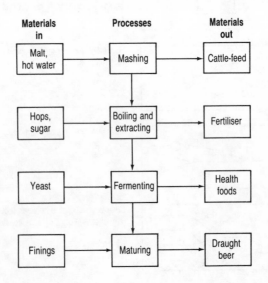

Figure 7.4 Specifying where material enters and leaves the brewing process

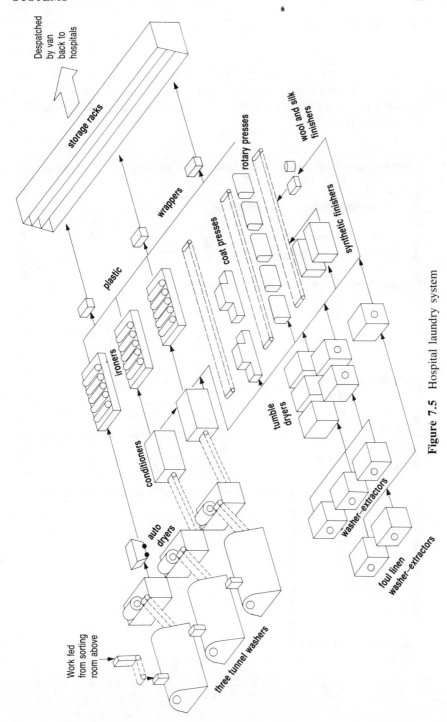

Figure 7.5 Hospital laundry system

Layout Maps

The hospital laundry had plenty of space and so could design a logical layout of machines. Also, storage was neatly separated from processing. Suppose that conditions are more cramped and machines cannot be moved to a more rational location. Figure 7.6 shows how this could complicate the material flow.

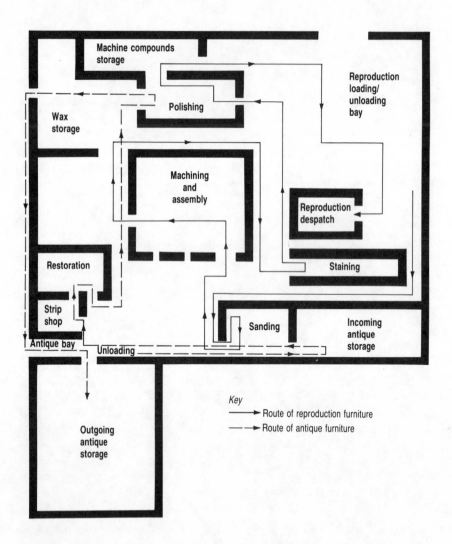

Figure 7.6 Scale diagram of the premises of a furniture renovator and manufacturer
(Paul Wilson Ltd)

Cycles of Handling Activity

So far, we have considered only the movement and storage of material. Suppose that transport equipment is also moving, sometimes loaded, sometimes returning unloaded. Figure 7.7 shows how this can be represented.

In the manufacture of crisps there is a central flow of activities associated with the movement of raw material — potatoes. Servicing this main flow there will be a subsidiary flow of handling equipment, sometimes running parallel, sometimes in a reverse direction to the main flow. So in Figure 7.7 the flow of crates, a truck, and a fork-lift are also accounted for. Apart from these, there is quite a variety of handling equipment used by a large crisp manufacturer, water chutes, conveyors, elevators, vibrators, tanks, tubs, bags and boxes, all of which should be included in a full systems diagram.

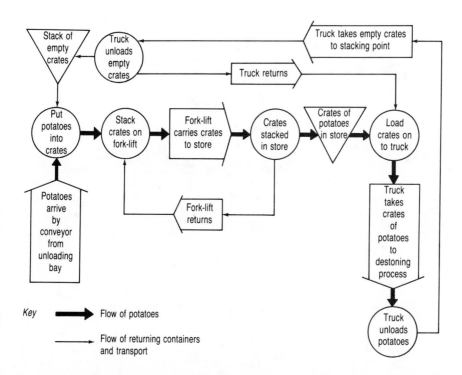

Figure 7.7 Part of a crisp-manufacturing process

Decision Points

It is convenient to identify those places in a system where you have to make a key decision. This is illustrated in Figure 7.8.

An Integrated Method Study Approach

There are two key activities that we have not yet brought into our illustrations – inspection and delay. If we add them, we will be using all the standard concepts employed by methods analysts. Figure 7.9 shows all these concepts in use.

The basic surgical situation is viewed very differently by the various participants:

- the patient
- the ward staff
- staff in the operating theatre

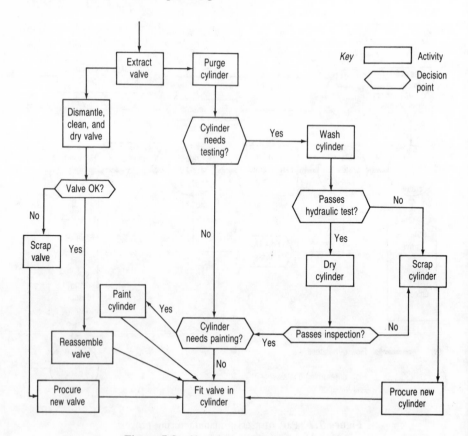

Figure 7.8 Changing a chlorine plant's valve

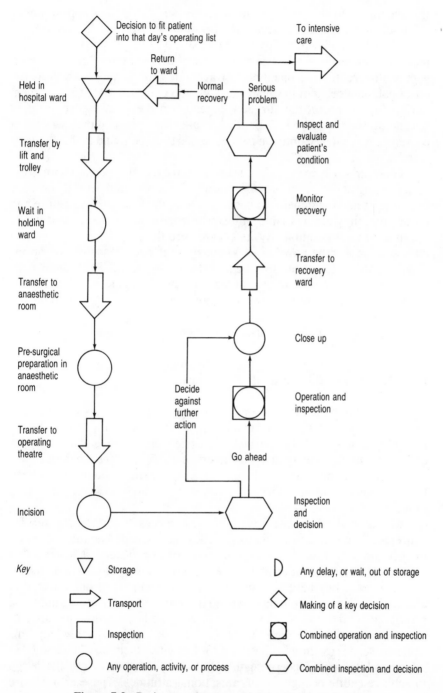

Figure 7.9 Basic procedures associated with hospital surgery

For example, to the patient, the anaesthetists's role may appear rather minimal. In fact, after rendering the patient unconscious, the anaesthetist and his or her staff will be involved in a string of major support activities until the patient recovers. The anaesthetist deals with the fluid and blood supply, the ventilating machine, intravenous drug supply as well as the continual monitoring of the heart rate and blood pressure. At every moment during the operation the surgeon depends on the anaesthetist to know whether the operation can continue. And after the operation the anaesthetist continues surveillance until the patient begins to come round in the recovery ward.

There are also many other hospital activities by specialists that the patients might not be aware of. Surgical support staff need to procure instruments and equipment for specific operations several days before and ensure that they are available in a sterile condition, correctly laid out at the time of the operation. By its very nature the time taken to complete an operation will be uncertain. Where there is a sequence of operations it will be difficult to keep to schedule. However, advance schedules need to be prepared because there is at least a 4-hour preparation time for the patient, so that last-minute substitutions are impossible. To complicate matters further, surgeons will be travelling between different hospitals, so scheduling their time is also important.

Effective Co-ordination of a System

The surgical example shows how important it is for a team to get its act together. Any mistakes or delays during a patient's operation could have fatal consequences. Other service industries also achieve a high degree of co-ordination to satisfy their customers, e.g. High-Street banking, supermarket retailing or airline booking. Traditionally, manufacturing has been less responsive, often with long unnecessary delays between placing an order and receiving it.

Recently, the Japanese have had great success installing the service concept into manufacturing industry. They have speeded up their response to customers by a major revamp of the operating system: deliveries that are smaller, more regular and more frequent, lower stocks and shorter set-up times. They have also introduced new methods of documentation and control. For example there are strict limits on material waiting to be processed by the use of Kanban cards which 'flow against the current' of material passing through the system. These are the visible symptoms of Japanese success in what has become known as their Just-In-Time (JIT) business philosophy. Underlying this philosophy is the use of systems design to achieve subtle changes in organisational attitudes. These changes are illustrated in the Push and Pull experiments that follow.

The Push and Pull System Experiments

Preparations

These experiments need between nine and fifteen people and take under an hour. You need the following equipment:

- A roll of small plastic poly bags.
- A stack of small cards, tickets or paper slips.
- Lots of Lego. You need enough to make 15 identical models containing between 20 and 40 bits. The model may look like a car, house or any other recognisable shape. Design a model that is quite challenging to construct but quite easy to inspect for correctness. In the first, the Push experiment, you use the poly bags and fifteen models. In the second, the Pull experiment, you use the poly bags, cards and twelve models.

The Push System Experiment

Layout   Use as large a room as possible. At three extremities of this room there will be three points where Lego models will be assembled. In the centre of the room will be a Production Control Unit as shown in Figure 7.10.

Assign two or three people to the Production Control Unit. Assign an equal number of people to each assembly team A, B, and C. Teams should contain four people or fewer.

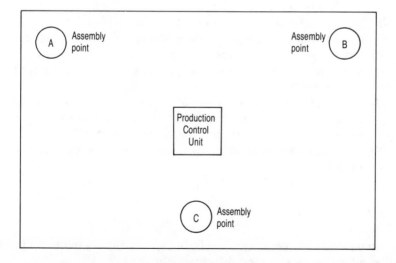

Figure 7.10   Layout for Push system experiment

Instructions to be followed by each team

(1) Each team will be given and must preserve a master model.
(2) Teams will receive from Production Control two plastic bags with Lego bits in them.
(3) Each plastic bag contains the exact parts to make a copy of the master model.
(4) Teams must convert bits from all the plastic bags given them into models. Only then can they take them for inspection.
(5) If any model is defective, that team must correct it before starting on any further assembly work.
(6) Production Control will keep a record of how many models each team has made. After a successful inspection, the leading team is given three bags of bits, the next team two bags, and the last team one bag. The team then returns to the assembly point and starts on a new cycle of work.

Production Control Unit's duties:

(1) Give each team a master model, retaining three masters for inspection purposes.
(2) In each of nine plastic bags put exactly the correct parts to make a model.
(3) Start the experiment by giving each team two bags of parts, retaining three bags as a buffer stock.
(4) Inspect a set of models brought to it by a team. Either approve the set, or send the team back to its assembly point to make corrections.
(5) Keep a cumulative tally of how many models each team has made (if there is a tie, the team reaching that score earliest is judged best).
(6) Give bags of parts to a team whenever it successfully passes an inspection: three bags to the leading team, two bags to the next, one bag to the last.
(7) Take completed models that have passed inspection, disassemble them and put them in plastic bags. Sometimes a team might have to wait whilst bags are being prepared for them.
(8) Stop the experiment when all three teams have together made 60 models.

The Pull System Experiment

If you have already completed the Push experiment, try a different model (of similar complexity) and different teams.

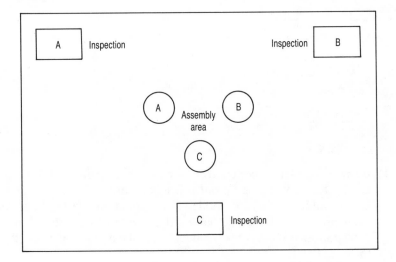

Figure 7.11 Layout for Pull system experiment

Layout Place inspection points at three extremities of a large room. Near the centre of the room, put three assembly points as shown in Figure 7.11.

Assign one inspector to each inspection station. Assign an equal number of people to each assembly team A, B and C. Teams should contain four people or fewer. In this experiment only twelve of the fifteen models are used. At each inspection point and each assembly point put one master model and one bag of disassembled bits. This uses up the twelve models. Only the instructions for team A are spelt out below because instructions for teams B and C are symmetric.

Team A's instructions

(1) Take a completed model to the A inspector.
(2) If the A inspector passes it, he gives the person who brought it a *pull Kanban card* (any ticket-shaped piece of card will do). Otherwise, the model must return to A's assembly point for correction.
(3) Take the Kanban card to the C inspector and exchange it for a plastic bag of Lego bits.
(4) Take the bag of bits back to A's assembly point, make a new model and repeat the cycle.

So the A carrier does a loop between these assembly points (circles) and inspections (squares):

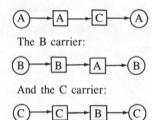

The B carrier:

And the C carrier:

Inspectors' duties

(1) Inspect completed models from the assembly point with the same label. If acceptable, give out a Kanban card.

(2) Disassemble completed models, put them in plastic bags and exchange a bag for a Kanban card delivered by another team.

A inspectors inspect A-team models, take them to bits and give them to team B.

B inspectors inspect B-team models, take them to bits and give them to team C.

C inspectors inspect C-team models, take them to bits and give them to team A.

(3) Someone should keep a tally of how many models have been made by all three teams. When this tally reaches 60, the experiment is stopped.

Review of the Experiments

The Push system has three noticeable components:

(i)   direct higher management control on the movement of material;

(ii)   incentives to the best team in terms of privileged material supply;

(iii)   implicitly, a spurring of the lesser teams to greater efforts by advertising the privileges available to the best.

By contrast, the Pull system operates in this way:

(i)   indirect management control of materials − if the Kanban system is obeyed, the workers themselves control material movement whilst keeping in-process stock at a minimum;

(ii)   incentives for the best team to improve the practices of their less efficient suppliers;

(iii)   implicitly, a chain reaction of co-operation spreading throughout the system.

If you carried out the Push and Pull experiments it is worth asking around among participants to see if they observed either of these traits:

(1) Under the Push system, was there a *downside Hawthorne effect?* I.e. 'If people who are doing badly are isolated and ignored, they lose interest and do worse. They are not motivated by observing other teams getting on like a house on fire.'

(*Note:* The Hawthorne effect derives from famous experiments on assemblers of electrical components, 1929–31. It is most often quoted as an upside effect: 'Good workers do even better if more attention is paid to them by supervisors.' Recently, the scientific method of the Hawthorne experiments has been questioned. Nevertheless Hawthorne redirected management's attention to a topic of primary importance: how to redesign the system to encourage motivation.)

(2) Under the Pull system was there a *learning curve* by *technology transfer?* I.e. when the experiments just started and assembly times were long, did the best group (frustrated by delays and finding themselves idle) pass on advice to the slower group?

Conclusion

These experiments show that fiercer control (a more stringent Push system) may not be the best way to higher efficiency. The alternative Pull system has much to commend it.

Note also that both the Push and Pull systems used the same product, same people and same process . . . yet can give very different results. This illustrates the critical importance of systems design in the operating process.

Contact Exercise

Arrange a visit to a production, service, transport or distribution operation and make a systems diagram of its processing and handling sequence.

The operation should be of reasonable size, approximately twenty employees or more. It is recommended that you do not tackle an operation with more than about 500 employees because of the complexity of the system.

A brief report should accompany your diagram, explaining the nature of the company and system. Discuss the major problems the company has, based on your interviews with staff and your observations.

Further Reading

Standard Texts

Burbidge (1971) Chapter 8.
Evans *et al.* (1987) Chapter 8.
Monks (1985) Chapter 3.
Schmenner (1987) Segment 1, (Plant Tours) and Chapter 4 (Kanban Systems).

Case Studies

Schmenner (1986) Carmen Canning Company.

Chapter 8

FORECASTING

Introduction

The operations manager needs forecasts for several reasons:

- (i)   to decide how to cope with the future volume of customer orders;
- (ii)   to react to the price and delivery availability of raw materials;
- (iii) to determine future machine and labour availabilities;
- (iv)   to respond to what is happening in the industry and the economy.

In operations management, forecasts and plans merge into statements of intent such as:

'This is how we are going to cope with a doubling of sales this year.'
'We'll earn 25% profit on that contract.'
'We must get three of these new machines.'

With these types of statement the forecaster is very much in a head-on-block situation. This is quite different from the detached, objective stance adopted by other forecasters.

The Demand Situation

Operating plans should be framed with a feeling for the stream of customer orders that is going to come into the business. It helps to classify these orders according to their size, timing and status. Size and timing are obvious enough concepts. But status needs a fuller explanation. Status falls into these categories:

(1) *Orders delivered but not yet paid for.* A small number of these might

be defective and need replacing or a rework. More significantly, you may wish to hold up the start of the next order for this customer until the outstanding payment has been made.

(2) *Orders actively being worked on.*
(3) *Contractually agreed orders that have not yet started.* If these have penalty clauses on delivery dates, care must be taken to provide the resources necessary to meet them and to avoid interference from other work.
(4) *Definite orders where final details have been settled.* With these, you may be able to negotiate delivery dates which fit in best with the other work that you have to do.
(5) *Customer inquiries and tenders submitted, neither of which have yet been translated into orders.*
(6) *Orders which your sales staff expect to materialise eventually.*
(7) *Nebulous orders.* Orders which have the habit of turning up out of the blue. Potential demand in an untapped market or from customers that you win from your competitors via a marketing campaign.

Items (5), (6) and (7) may appear to be in the realm of marketing staff. But the operations manager needs to have a rough idea about these areas so that he or she can plan future staffing and equipment levels. When operations managers view the future they should be wary of aggregating orders of a different status. Each of the seven statuses above have their own special effect on the planning activity of the firm.

Initial and Replacement Demand

Any manufacturer of durable goods should distinguish between initial (first-time) buyers and cyclical (replacement) buyers. Failure to do so has led to the collapse of firms providing new goods such as washing machines and personal computers.

Also failure to predict the correct growth of initial demand for a consumer durable can lead to serious planning consequences. For example, after the Second World War all the UK's road and housing programmes were based on the assumption that cars per head would increase from 1 per 100 to 2, perhaps 3 ... certainly no more than 6. This was confirmed by a series of independent statistical investigations between 1944 and 1951. A proper appreciation of the potential growth in cars did not occur until crude extrapolation was replaced by economic models. These showed that demand was highly elastic to changes in income, the price of cars and the cost and benefit of motoring.

The Supply Situation

There are a few internationally traded raw materials the price of which has a substantial impact on the activities of certain firms: e.g. sugar, grain and meats on food processing, metals on engineering, cotton and wool on clothing, and crude oil (directly or indirectly) on pretty well everything. Often producers of these materials enter into trading agreements (*cartels*) to control prices by a centralised buffer stock or output quota system. The best known of these are the OPEC oil-price agreements and the EEC farm-support system, but there are many other cartels in for example coffee, cocoa, sugar, copper and tin. The history of these cartels seems to follow a similar pattern. In the early days of a new agreement prices are kept artificially high. Because of these high prices, producer – members have the necessary funds to support a build-up of unsold stocks by a central administration. Eventually this buffer stock becomes so enormous that some members are no longer willing to pay their portion of the storage charges. When they withdraw from the scheme, some of the buffer stock has to be sold to avoid insolvency. This causes prices to plummet. Further instability is injected into raw material prices by major harvest variations and the use of cartels to secure political and military ends (especially with OPEC). In general, this means that the operations manager buying from a commodity cartel has to follow events day by day to avoid being caught by sudden major price changes.

Coping with Variations in the Business Environment

Operating managers should keep a tag on any general influence that might affect a firm, its industry, its market, its competitors or suppliers, for example by reading the daily financial press and the weekly or monthly trade journals. In addition, growing use is made of commercially operated data banks accessible from a distant computer terminal. These give up-to-the-minute information in chart, tabular or statistical-formula format. In many respects, there can be almost too much information coming into a business. One sign of a good manager is how well he or she filters, files, interprets and follows up the stream of incoming stimuli. A balance must be struck between:

(i)   a restless exploration of all new items and letting day-to-day work slip;

(ii)   regarding all news, informal contacts and peripheral activities as distractions from the job in hand, thus missing out on a few new opportunities.

How should an operating manager cope with disruptions such as random weather or accident factors? One way is to determine the optimal response time between news of a disruption and taking action. For example lives can be saved by cutting a few minutes off the lead time between forecasting fog and placing warning signs and extra traffic cones on motorways. Another approach is to use forecast frequencies of occurrence to determine the allocation of resources (e.g. more snowploughs should be allocated to Scotland than an area of equivalent population and size in southern England).

Seasonality

By definition, disruptions spring on you by surprise. But there are ways of dealing with seasonality, i.e. regular variations of some activity over any identifiable cycle. Where the activity is consumer demand, the seasonal cycle might be daily (gas demand), weekly (shopping) or yearly (package holidays). Other aspects of seasonality may be highlighted by asking these questions:

How regular is the seasonal cycle? It may be fixed absolutely (special activities tied in to Sundays), slightly variable (the timing of winter weather) or elastic (the interval between flu epidemics).

What is the cause of the variation? For consumer demand this may be tied tightly to another very predictable variable (e.g. electric lighting to the hours of darkness). Or the demand might be tied tightly to a slightly more unpredictable variable (e.g. ice-cream sales to average summer temperatures). Or the demand, though following a cyclical pattern, may have no obvious explanation (e.g. changing lengths of skirts in fashion).

Where reliable data are available over several seasons, the seasonal effect can be quantified either as an actual or as a proportionate variation from the average. Where there is little shift in a long-run average, the method of calculating seasonal deviations from it is easy. Consider the example in Table 8.1.

Often, the calculation of the seasonal variation is not that easy. There may be no steady average because of the existence of certain long-run plateau shifts and trends. With hindsight, everyone knows what a trend is — a long-term, gradual shift in the average value. But there is some doubt about the legitimacy of projecting a trend into the future. In the words of Sir Alec Cairncross:

> A trend is a trend is a trend
> But the question is, will it bend?

Table 8.1 UK live births per quarter (000s)

	I	II	III	IV	Yearly total
1980	186	193	193	182	
1981	180	185	189	177	731
1982	176	180	186	176	718
1983	175	185	187	174	721
1984	176	181	191	181	729
1985	183	189	197	182	751
1986	182	194	194	184	
Average	178	184	190	178	
Actual quarterly deviation	−4.5	+1.5	+7.5	−4.5	
% deviation	−2.5	+0.8	+4.1	−2.5	

Note: The actual quarterly deviations for 1981−5 are from a grand yearly average of 182.5. Note also 1980 and 1986 data were not used in calculating averages and deviations. They were included here so that you can use them for prior and post data in later exercises.

> Will it alter its course,
> Through some unforeseen force
> And come to a premature end?

A very apt comment on the smooth trend in share prices before the October 1987 stock market crash.

A good example of the complex interaction between trends and plateau shifts is the recent variation in the number of UK road deaths. There is an upward trend resulting from wider car ownership and a sharp shift to a lower plateau value after the introduction of seat-belt legislation. Also there is the effect of extending breathalyser tests (lower plateau), greater alcohol consumption (upward trend) and an ageing population (causing two opposite trends: older people drive more safely but don't recover so easily after an accident). In spite of all these complex factors, a reasonable estimation of seasonal variation can be made by comparing actual data to a moving average, as shown in Table 8.2.

The moving averages were calculated according to this formula:

$$M_t = \frac{1}{4}(\frac{1}{2}A_{t-2} + A_{t-1} + A_t + A_{t+1} + \frac{1}{2}A_{t+2})$$

where t = the relevant time period
A_t = Actual road deaths at time t
M_t = Moving average at time t

Only moving averages for 1981−5 were calculated. Actual road deaths in 1980 and 1986 were included to help with the calculations and for later reference.

Table 8.2 Actual and moving average (bracketed) UK road deaths per quarter

	I	II	III	IV
1980	1,369	1,422	1,556	1,606
1981	1,311 (1,411)	1,331 (1,461)	1,593 (1,461)	1,611 (1,467)
1982	1,310 (1,474)	1,382 (1,479)	1,596 (1,472)	1,644 (1,450)
1983	1,227 (1,411)	1,287 (1,367)	1,377 (1,340)	1,513 (1,333)
1984	1,144 (1,354)	1,312 (1,386)	1,519 (1,390)	1,624 (1,368)
1985	1,071 (1,337)	1,207 (1,305)	1,373 (1,301)	1,514 (1,314)
1986	1,155	1,225	1,396	1,027

Directly from Table 8.2 you can calculate:
actual seasonal deviations $(A_t - M_t)$ and
percentage seasonal deviations $= 100\ (A_t - M_t)/M_t$.
These are shown in Table 8.3.

Table 8.3 Actual seasonal and percentage seasonal (bracketed) variations

	I	II	III	IV
1981	−100 (− 7.1%)	−130 (−8.9%)	+132 (+9.0%)	+144 (+ 9.8%)
1982	−164 (−11.1%)	− 97 (−6.6%)	+124 (+8.4%)	+194 (+13.4%)
1983	−184 (−13.0%)	− 80 (−5.9%)	+ 37 (+2.8%)	+180 (+13.5%)
1984	−210 (−15.5%)	− 74 (−5.3%)	+129 (+9.3%)	+256 (+18.7%)
1985	−266 (−19.9%)	− 98 (−7.5%)	+ 72 (+5.5%)	+200 (+15.2%)

Table 8.3 reveals a fairly consistent seasonal pattern. You could continue the analysis by finding an average seasonal variation for each column. But before doing that it is worth studying individual variations to see how they fit in with breathalyser and seat-belt campaigns or even unusual weather. In fact if you compare Table 8.4 with Table 8.3 you will see a surprising association: road accidents in the first quarter appear to drop when the weather is severe! This analysis of road deaths illustrates the desirability of searching for causes beyond the time series under study. This can be done by advanced forecasting techniques of multiple regression or economic modelling. But to work well, these methods need access to 'lengthy and accurate time series with certain special statistical properties. Finally, it should be noted that identifying the seasonal factor is more than an end in itself. It provides a most convenient starting point for the discovery of other causes.

Exercise

Carry out a seasonal analysis on the time series in Table 8.4.

Table 8.4 England and Wales quarterly average temperatures (°C)

	I	II	III	IV
1980	4.9	11.5	15.5	7.5
1981	5.7	11.2	15.2	6.1
1982	5.2	12.2	16.0	8.0
1983	5.5	10.8	17.0	8.5
1984	4.0	11.1	16.1	9.1
1985	3.0	10.9	15.4	7.6
1986	3.0	10.8	14.0	8.7

Hindsight Evaluation of Forecasts

How can you check whether one forecasting technique is better than another? It all depends on how you evaluate the deviations, or errors, between forecast and actual. We will follow the normal practice of letting 'errors' and 'deviation' mean the same thing in this context.

The three most common ways of summarising deviations are:

- BIAS (arithmetic average of deviations)
- MAD (mean of absolute deviations)
- MSE (mean of squared errors)

Example: Daily Bread Demand

At the end of each day, a bread shop has to forecast next day's demand so that the central bakery knows how much to deliver to the bread shop next morning. Table 8.5 shows the forecast, the actual demand and the calculation of the three basic audit devices.

Table 8.5

	Week 1						Week 2						Sum	Sum/12	Averages
	M	T	W	T	F	S	M	T	W	T	F	S	Sum	12	Averages
Forecast	75	64	67	65	66	93	76	54	70	61	64	85	840	70	= Average forecast
Actual demand	75	60	73	64	71	97	79	53	66	59	72	95	864	72	= Average demand
Error + or −	0	+4	−6	+1	−5	−4	−3	+1	+4	+2	−8	−10	−24	−2	= BIAS
Absolute deviation	0	4	6	1	5	4	3	1	4	2	8	10	48	4	= MAD
(Error)^2	0	16	36	1	25	16	9	1	16	4	64	100	288	24	= MSE

Tracking signals   These signals check on whether there is any significant change in the forecasting error. Tracking signals lie at the heart of advanced forecasting methods and can be accumulations, weights, ratios or statistical distributions. Table 8.6 gives a popular procedure for calculating a simple tracking signal from the previous bread shop data.

Table 8.6

	W	T	F	S	M	T	W	T	F	S
Total of last three (+ or −) errors = X	−2	−1	−10	−8	−12	−6	+2	+7	−2	−16
Total of last three absolute deviations = Y	10	11	12	10	12	8	8	7	14	20
Tracking signal = 3X/Y	−0.6	−0.3	−2.5	−2.4	−3.0	−2.3	0.75	3.0	−0.4	−2.4

The way this particular tracking signal is constructed, it could swing from -3 to $+3$ according to the level of underforecasting or over-forecasting. The main value of tracking signals is in automatic techniques handled by a computer without human intervention. (See also the 'ROQ/ROL' example in Chapter 9.)

Any forecasting should seek a balance between the cost of making an overforecast and the perhaps very different cost of making an under-forecast. It is rare for any exposition of BIAS, MAD, MSE or tracking signal to consider this issue.

For example, *a supermarket selling bread taken from a freezer* has trivial costs from overstocking (electricity and freezer-space charges). But bread is often used as a loss leader to attract people into a store to do all their weekend shopping. If the supermarket is seen to run out of bread (say) lunchtime Saturday, people will go elsewhere for all their purchases, and they might be deterred from shopping at that supermarket the following week. So we could have something like: cost of overstocking 2p, cost of understocking £2.00, per loaf.

A village store selling fresh bread has bigger costs from overstocking. Any bread unsold at the end of the day will go stale and be near-worthless. But if the village store is the only one, and has captive customers, it will not lose their goodwill for other purchases if it understocks. All it will lose is the profit margin on the loaf. So, for the village store the cost of overstocking is more likely to be 30p, the cost of understocking 10p, per loaf.

Suppose we take these village store overstocking/understocking costs and apply them to the errors occurring in the previous bread shop example, as shown in Table 8.7.

Table 8.7

	M	T	W	T	F	S	M	T	W	T	F	S	Total
Forecasting error	0	+4	−6	+1	−5	−4	−3	+1	+4	+2	−8	−10	
Cost of over-forecast at 30p/unit		120		30				30	120	60			360
Cost of under-forecast at 10p/unit			60		50	40	30				80	100	360

Look at the most serious individual forecasting errors on a cost basis (e.g. the 120). These do not tie up with the most serious individual 'errors' as identified by the BIAS, MAD and (especially) MSE components.

Look at the total cost of under- and overforecasting (each 360). That is a nice balance. Compare that with the supposed 'BIAS' in the mathematical audits.

What general conclusions can be drawn up from this example? MSE is only remotely connected with cost effects and should never be used by an operations manager. If costs are not available and there is no obvious 'under and over' distortion, it is fairly safe to use BIAS and MAD.

Forecasting by Formula

Using only the past data of a time series, what is the best formula for predicting its future value? This has been extensively discussed by statisticians. Their findings? In short ... 'It all depends on the time series.'

If we had to select three formulae which we thought were best, this would be our choice:

(1) *Last Period's Actual:*

$$F_{t+1} = A_t$$

This very simple formula can beat all-comers when there is a continuous trade-off between current and future values (e.g. for Stock Exchange share prices).

(2) *Last-Change Scaling:*

$$F_{t+1} = A_t + k (A_t - A_{t-1})$$

This formula copes well with elementary trends and oscillations.

(3) *Double Exponential Smoothing:*

$$F_{t+1} = S_t + T_t$$
where $S_t = \alpha A_t + (1 - \alpha) F_t$, and
$$T_t = \beta (S_t - S_{t-1}) + (1 - \beta) T_{t-1}$$

This formula frequently beats more sophisticated rivals in forecasting competitions.

Symbols used in the three forecasting formulae are as follows:

t = time period
A_t = actual value
F_t = forecasted value
k = scaling coefficient of last change
α = exponential smoothing coefficient of 'actuals'
β = exponential smoothing coefficients of the trend

When applying these formulae to a time series, there are two ways of finding the best k, α and β to use:

(1) Take a set of past data and experiment, using whatever coefficient(s) gives the lowest MAD (Mean Absolute Deviation) for the whole test series.

(2) Start by giving the coefficients arbitrary values. Calculate cumulative MADs both for the coefficient values you have chosen and for some nearby coefficient values. If any of them has a better cumulative MAD switch to this better coefficient. Continue, switching further if necessary. Eventually you will settle down to the same values as in (1), but you have been more honest in that you have not taken advantage of future information. This is called *adaptive forecasting*.

Exercise 1

Apply the three formulae to the 'Births' time series of Table 8.1. Before applying the formula, deseasonalise the data as suggested by the text in the Seasonality section. Use coefficients of $k = -0.4$, $\alpha = -0.7$ and $\beta = 0.1$. Evaluate, via MAD, which of the three forecasting formulae is best.

Exercise 2

In Exercise 1 you were given coefficients which happened to be best possible ones. Now find the best coefficients yourself when applying the formulae to deseasonalised road accidents. What is the best formula (use MAD to judge)?

Exercise 3

Assuming that you did the deseasonalising exercise on the 'Weather' series in the earlier section, apply the same analysis

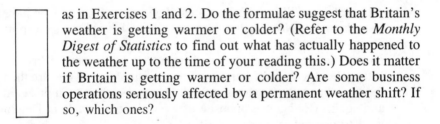

as in Exercises 1 and 2. Do the formulae suggest that Britain's weather is getting warmer or colder? (Refer to the *Monthly Digest of Statistics* to find out what has actually happened to the weather up to the time of your reading this.) Does it matter if Britain is getting warmer or colder? Are some business operations seriously affected by a permanent weather shift? If so, which ones?

A General Note on Forecasting by Formula

There are certain strengths and weaknesses to the formula approach. It is obsessively neutral. It is not concerned about whether the time interval is days, months or years. Nor is it influenced by the thing being forecast; it could equally well be apples, sunspots or polar bears. It analyses a single stream of numbers divorced from any discussion about what they mean, how they were generated, or how accurate they are. There is no search for leading indicators, associations or causes other than within the time series itself.

In a way, formula forecasting could be rechristened *Count of Monte Cristo forecasting*. Imagine you had been imprisoned for years in solitary confinement. Suppose you were fed streams of unidentified (but not random) numbers by your gaoler, who, for your torment or pleasure, asks 'Guess the next number?'

Mathematicians have developed advanced techniques for handling this very special situation. Occasionally, one of these techniques is useful to the operations manager (e.g. simple autoregression for repurchase depending on the age of an item such as a car). But mostly you will find that the three simple techniques which we have suggested are quite adequate if you need to do this sort of thing. That last phrase was an important qualification. 'Monte Cristo' forecasting should be tried only as a last resort, when nothing can be found out about causation.

Groupthink Forecasting

This is most applicable to long-range issues where there could be conflict during the decision-making process (e.g. building the Channel Tunnel, introducing a vaccine with possible side-effects, or pretty well any big political decision). More often the operations manager has these decisions passed on to him or her rather than being directly involved. Nevertheless the manager should be aware of some rather innovative groupthink techniques.

(1) *Jury panels* A bit like a courtroom, there is an advocate for a

proposal, a devil's advocate against it and a small panel who have
to make a Yes/No decision when they have heard both sides plus
cross-examinations.

(2) *Delphi circles* Experts, isolated from each other, make forecasts
(often about long-term impacts of new technology). They are then
fed the other experts' views and asked to revise their opinion again
and again. (Rather the opposite of what the old Oracle at Delphi
used to do, but let that pass.)

(3) *Scenarios* As a starting point, you have to accept that the world
tomorrow is very different from today, however improbable − e.g.
that the Antarctic icecap has melted − then you follow through the
consequences of that assumption.

(4) *Interactive gaming* Role-playing in an unstable situation − usually
where there will be only one winner, who cannot be predicted by
conventional means.

Forecasting Advisers

It is difficult to find impartial advisers:

(1) Advisers have a vested interest in your decision. For a big capital
project, the people who forecast costs and revenues for the initial
feasibility study may also be involved in tendering for the job *if*
it is to go ahead.

(2) Suppose advisers are aware of the answer you would like to hear
from them. There is a temptation for them to provide that answer,
solely because they will be looked upon favourably the next time
you want consulting work done.

(3) Advisers may be well known in their profession for a committed
stance on some issue. Even if they now feel doubtful about that
stance they will still maintain it to avoid the charge of inconsistency.

Summary

Successful operational forecasters are alert and on top of events. For them,
forecasting and planning are intertwined. There are two traps that the
practical forecaster must avoid:

(i)   going overboard with the mathematical techniques;
(ii)   relying on judgemental methods alone.

Also, it is good practice to install a system to monitor the accuracy of
forecasts and to evaluate the cost to the firm of getting forecasts wrong.

Further Reading

Standard Texts

Adam and Ebert (1986) Chapter 5.
Burbidge (1971) Chapter 15.
Lewis (1981) Chapters 14 and 15.
Lockyer (1975) Chapters 4 and 5.
McLain and Thomas (1980) Chapter 7.
Stevenson (1986) Chapter 3.

Specialist Texts

Armstrong, J.S. (1978) *Long Range Forecasting,* 2nd edn, Wiley. A misnomer. All sorts of forecasts covered. Very eclectic. A book to dip into again and again. Good sense. Good fun.

Case Studies

Meier (1982) Midcentral.
Nicholson (1978) Speedcraft Transport; Adams Ice Cream.

Chapter 9

OPERATIONAL PLANNING

Introduction

Operational planning covers all the planning activities of the firm. Starting from knowledge of a firm's capabilities and market potential, there is a downward process of planning which ends up with precise instructions telling every worker what to do next. Obtaining these instructions involves the application of a variety of techniques associated with *scheduling* and *inventory control*.

Objectives of Operational Planning

The *primary objective* can be easily stated: 'to attain the best long-run stream of profits'.

But there is quite a gap between what the planner, inventory manager or scheduler does today, and how this influences the profit and loss account perhaps several months later. For this reason a planner must work to certain *secondary objectives,* minimising:

- the processing time of a customer's order
- a machine's idle time
- time wasted when an operative is waiting for work
- stocks of raw materials
- stocks of work in progress
- stocks of finished goods

Often, these secondary objectives are totalled or averaged to get *tertiary objectives*. And the process does not stop there, as, at the *fourth level*, the scheduler is judged on how well he or she shapes up to certain ratios or weightings of tertiary objectives, or how differences between actual and forecast are minimised, or how closely one keeps to a cumulative schedule over time. Sometimes planning by higher-level objectives overlooks, or works against, the primary objective of the firm. So in our opinion methods of planning should always bear in mind the firm's cash-flow situation.

From Aggregate Planning to the Master Production Schedule

Aggregate Planning concerns all aspects of a firm's business. It covers a major planning period such as a quarter, year or quinquennium. It reviews the firm's strengths and weaknesses, opportunities and threats, and recommends what business to go for. Such planning has implications for many parts of a business, e.g. marketing, finance or administration. It has particular interest for the operating manager in that it lays the groundwork for the *Master Production Schedule* (MPS).

The MPS is the channel through which customer orders are funnelled to the workplace. It provides the background information to tell the worker what to make, how much to make and when to make it. When the MPS is constructed, it seeks a balance between:

(i)   the size, timing and status of customer orders;
(ii)   the resources, loads and capacities of the operating system.

In small manufacturing firms there is often an early Monday morning meeting every week or fortnight to sketch an MPS over their *planning horizon* (i.e. until they meet for the next MPS). After an MPS has been sketched out, the finer details will be filled in and monitored by a scheduler in consultation with supervisors.

The length of the planning horizon varies between industries. Wholesalers, supermarkets and general practitioners often reset their MPS daily. A construction firm might do this only quarterly. In education the interval is even larger, in effect the year between course enrolments.

Customer Priorities and the MPS

Assembling of an MPS should have marketing factors very much in mind, in particular the priority that is given to customers. If the MPS does not establish its authority in this matter, works managers will be tempted to change schedules when put under pressure by impatient customers who phone them up directly; or expediters will scurry round speeding up urgent jobs when such jobs should have been identified in the first place by the

MPS. Short-run measures should always be subservient to the MPS, which strikes an overall balance between resources and customers.

In achieving this balance there should be a subtle evaluation of customers. Two customers who appear to have submitted identical orders should not be treated equally. One order may have been placed late, asked for early, or come from a notoriously slow payer. Or one firm may have more stringent quality checks than another. Or one firm may be about to place another big order if the current order progresses satisfactorily. For all these reasons and others (connected with internal scheduling matters) the original *customer order numbers* assigned when the sales department receives an order might have to be juggled around very differently when the MPS assigns *works order numbers*.

Constructing a Very Simple MPS

Consider a service that cannot be stored — transport services, for example. Figure 9.1 shows an MPS for a freight haulier. Each asterisk '*' shows a unit of surplus capacity indicating that new business must be found, or the

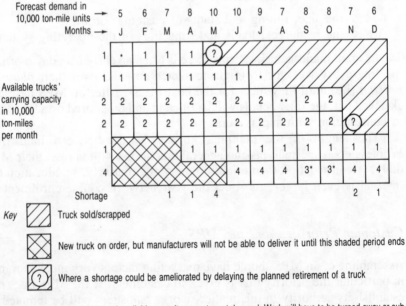

Figure 9.1 Simple MPS for a freight haulier

truck and driver sidelined. The asterisk in July shows that there is a case for retiring a truck earlier than August as planned.

The above system, though elementary, is quite sufficient for the rough-cut nature of the MPS. And quite satisfactory schedules can be generated by referring to a mixture of priority rules, such as:

'Retire an old vehicle before a new vehicle.'
'Don't plan to retire an old vehicle until two months after its replacement has been delivered.'
'Never subcontract out work for a new important customer.'
'Even though bigger lorries have cheaper unit costs, keep a reasonable mixture of sizes to help the scheduler when he later has to do his daily juggling act.'

Constructing a More Elaborate MPS

These are the extra features that might have to be included:

(i)   making for stock as well as supplying to order;
(ii)   holding over spare capacity for urgent new orders;
(iii)   anticipating future orders;
(iv)   handling plant shutdowns;
(v)   distinguishing different operating conditions (introducing a new shift, or setting a general limit on overtime working).

If you wish to incorporate all these features, it is necessary to have a matrix with time on both axes, as shown in Figure 9.2.

After the blank table has been designed, rough-cut estimates of capacities and forward orders are set down (those numbers shown to the left and above the central cells in the table). Finally, allocations are made to cells within the table so that rows and columns 'balance'. Note that the bottom two rows and the final column can act as sumps to mop up any imbalances.

Both this MPS and the earlier simple one could be 'optimised' by assigning cost or revenues per unit to each cell. But we would strongly advise against it for the following reasons. This Master Production Schedule involves key strategic decisions about things like:

(i)   how much work to give subcontractors;
(ii)   what levels of overtime to aim for;
(iii)   how many own-products to make.

Management will make these decisions according to 'business feel' and will not be dictated to by a computational process based on inappropriate accounting estimates.

For example, management will take on business in a depression so

		Customers' Forward Orders, Received or (Expected)						25 Make and Stock Own Products	(32) Standby for Urgent Orders	Reserve Capacity
		25 Jan.	25 Feb.	(10) +20 Mar.	(20) +10 Apr.	(20) May	(30) Jun.			
Jan.	Shift I 25	12	8	5						
	Shift II 15	8		7						
	Overtime	5								
Feb.	Shift I 25	///	12					8	(5)	
	Shift II 15	///		8+(4)					(3)	
	Overtime	///	5							
Mar.	Plant Shutdown	///	///	///	///	///	///	///	///	///
Apr.	Shift I 25	///	///	///	10+(2)				(8)	5
	Shift II	///	///	///	///	///	///	///	///	///
	Overtime	///	///	///	///	///	///	///	///	5
May	Shift I 25	///	///	///	///	(10)	(5)	10		
	Shift II 15	///	///	///	///	(10)			(5)	
	Overtime	///	///	///	///	///			(3)	2
Jun.	Shift I 25	///	///	///	///	///	(15)	5	(5)	
	Shift II 15	///	///	///	///	///	(10)	2	(3)	
	Overtime	///	///	///	///	///	///	///	///	///
Work taken but subcontracted out		///	///		(10)			///	///	///
Work refused				(6)	(8)			///	///	

Production Capacity labels the rows Jan.–Jun.

Key ⧄ Impossible allocations which are filled in before the planners do anything else

Figure 9.2 MPS for a sleeping-bag manufacturer (all items in units of ten sleeping bags)

long as they feel it will cover marginal costs and/or lead to future business. And they will reject quite profitable work in a boom if they think that even more profitable work is round the corner. When difficult issues such as these arise it is best to analyse them via a simple communicable framework.

The MPS and Product Variety

The examples we have used were drawn from firms with an unusually simple product range. The freight haulier shifting bulk commodities can use ton-miles as a good indication of his efficiency and profit, even if he is transporting many different products. Likewise a sleeping bag is a fairly uniform item and if this was all that was manufactured, the MPS would be easy to construct. In fact, sleeping bags accounted for only 60 per cent of the turnover of this particular firm as tents and outdoor clothing were also manufactured.

Under these circumstances, the table has to be expanded and the units of measurement changed. Now we will have:

(i) customer orders for each product per period in unit quantities;
(ii) shift hours worked;
(iii) in the body of the table, conversion factors showing how many hours are needed to make each product.

Figure 9.3 shows how this works for just part of the previous table.

To conclude, the MPS is a key document that should be simple to

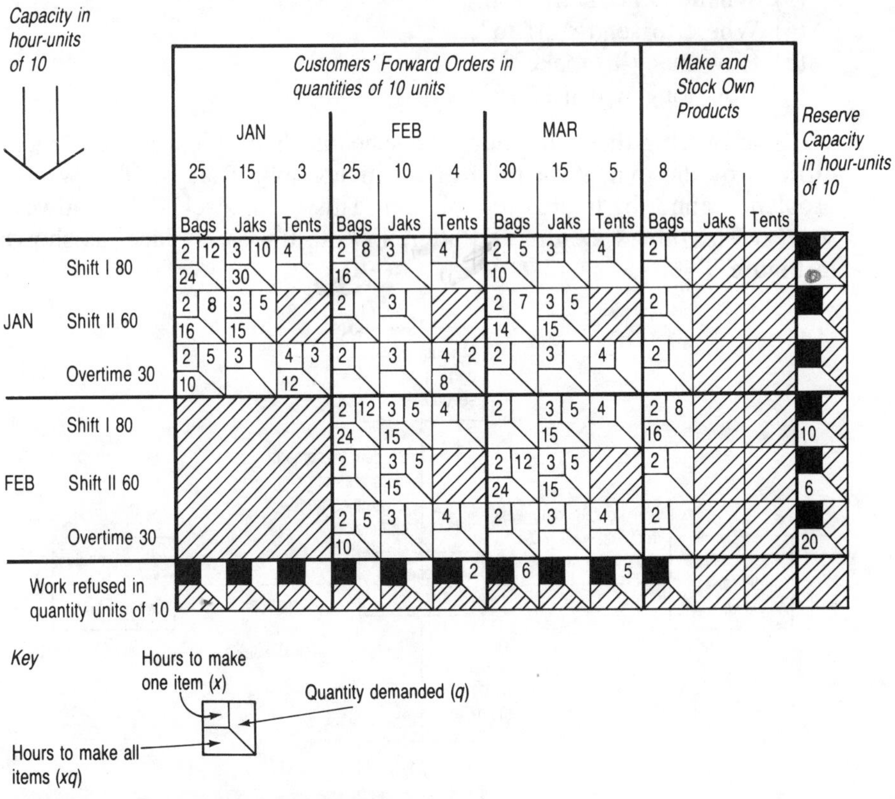

All numbers below a diagonal must balance across a row
All numbers above a diagonal must balance down a column
Note: Shift II workers were not skilled enough to make tents; only bags were made for stock.

Figure 9.3 MPS for sleeping-bag manufacturer including other product varieties construct and understand. However, where there is product variety, you cannot avoid handling the conversion process from marketing's *revenue or quantity* figures to production's *utilisation* criteria such as hours worked. Without such a conversion you cannot relate an MPS to capacity.

Operational Scheduling

Introduction

Schedulers take rough-cut MPSs and put them into practice.
    Working schedules determine these questions:

(1) What to do?
(2) Who is to do it?
(3) Where to get stuff from?
(4) Where to send stuff to?
(5) How many to make?
(6) How long will it take?

In answering these questions the scheduler's problem is made more difficult by the dynamic nature of his or her job. That is, 'this week's problem' cannot be treated in isolation. This week's schedule is always squeezed by others, before and after, in both time and place, as shown in Figure 9.4.

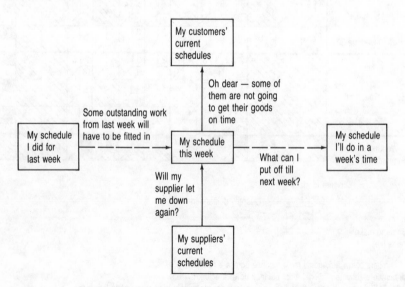

Figure 9.4 The scheduler's problem

Also, there are other interference factors which make scheduling difficult:

(1) Scheduling instructions have to be combined with other documents serving different purposes, for example inspection or payment records.
(2) Schedulers have to calculate and communicate via numbers and writing. But many operatives only really respond to verbal communications and also tend to memorise things rather than file documents.
(3) The scheduler rarely gets free access or perfect feedback from the workplace. The schedule may get altered by on-the-spot foremen, or operatives may be careless in filling in a record of work completed.

In particular the scheduler rarely has up-to-date knowledge of materials in the system. There have been two recent developments which have attempted to improve this situation.

Cycle counting   Here, people are employed to count stock full time, every day of the year, not just at a stocktaking. They use calculators with disk memories that a computer can analyse later. As their objective is to help management decisions rather than to audit, they do not need to be precise or exhaustive in their work. Instead, they have developed certain heuristics to maximise their effectiveness e.g. to count high-value-turnover items more frequently, or to count stock at its low point just before a new order is delivered.

Bar coding   In the public mind, bar codes are associated with supermarket checkouts and credit cards. It is not surprising that bar codes were quick to be adopted by library and security services. More surprising, perhaps, is their use in the health service, especially for blood banks, and their now widespread attachment to all components on car assembly lines. Initially, use of bar codes was hampered by the high cost of the equipment needed to read a code and the software to operate it (e.g. £2,000 for a high-quality supermarket checkout machine). But costs are falling sharply, dropping to £200 at the lower end of the market. This opens up enormous potential for the adoption of bar codes in all operating systems, providing instant feedback for all material in process.

Having discussed the general background we now describe some specific scheduling techniques.

Inventory Scheduling 1: Re-order Quantity/Re-order Level Stocking Policies (ROQ/ROL)

This is inventory control with minimum human intervention. Once management has set rules about when to re-order and how much, the system pretty well runs itself. It has developed from the *two-bin* or *place-card* method of inventory control, i.e. the method where, if you drew stock from the top of a box downwards, at a certain point near the bottom you would find a reply-paid card from your supplier saying 'Stocks are running low. Post this off to us today and we will send you another box.' In its more sophisticated form, big retailers have bar coded all their items. Every time an item is sold, a message is sent to a central computer which keeps a running total of how many items the store has left. When the running total drops below a certain level, alarm bells in the computer cause it to send off an automatic message to a central warehouse or a manufacturer saying 'Make another delivery of so much of this item to this store.' *If* subtle rules can be fed into the computer, much clerical effort can be saved.

However, great care is needed in designing even the simplest automatic system. As a minimum requirement, an ROQ/ROL system should be able to cope with:

(i)   variable demand
(ii)   variable lead times
(iii)   handling stockouts
(iv)   uncertainty about future orders

Figures 9.5, 9.6 and 9.7 demonstrate how to handle these situations.

Explanation of the ROQ/ROL Tables

The table in Figure 9.5 is mostly blank. It shows all the information coming into the system from outside (i.e. demand, lead time and first period's opening stock). After you have made up rules about

ROL (when to re-order) and
ROQ (how much to re-order)

every remaining number in the table can be filled in, from period 1 to period 20. Then you can evaluate your solution to see how good it is. This has been fully worked through in Figure 9.6 (simple) and Figure 9.7 (a little advanced).

Lead Time tells you how long you have to wait before an order is delivered. To simulate the real situation assume you know the lead time operating from the beginning of the period that you are in, but that you do not know

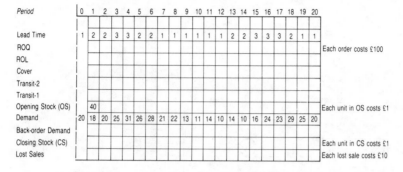

Period	0	1	2	3	4	5	6	7	8	9	10	11	12	13	14	15	16	17	18	19	20	
Lead Time	1	2	2	3	3	2	2	1	1	1	1	1	1	2	2	3	3	3	2	1	1	
ROQ																						Each order costs £100
ROL																						
Cover																						
Transit-2																						
Transit-1																						
Opening Stock (OS)		40																				Each unit in OS costs £1
Demand	20	18	20	25	31	26	28	21	22	13	11	14	10	14	10	16	24	23	29	25	20	
Back-order Demand																						
Closing Stock (CS)																						Each unit in CS costs £1
Lost Sales																						Each lost sale costs £10

Figure 9.5 ROQ/ROL table

Period	0	1	2	3	4	5	6	7	8	9	10	11	12	13	14	15	16	17	18	19	20	
Lead Time	1	2	2	3	3	2	2	1	1	1	1	1	1	2	2	3	3	3	2	1	1	
ROQ = 30		(30)	(30)		(30)	(30)	(30)	(30)			(30)		(30)			(30)	(30)		(30)			11 orders @ £100 = £1,100
ROL = 60		60	60	60	60	60	60	60	60	60	60	60	60	60	60	60	60	60	60	60	60	
Cover		40*	52*	62	37*	6*	60*	60*	99	77	64	53*	69	59*	75	65	49*	55*	62	60		
Transit-2					(30)													(30)	(30)			
Transit-1		(30)	(30)			(60)	(30)						(30)				(30)	(30)				
Opening Stock		40	22	(32)	(37)	6	0	(60)	(99)	77	64	53	(69)	59	45	(65)	49	25	2	(30)	(60)	894 units @ £1 = £ 894
Demand	20	18	20	25	31	26	28	21	22	13	11	14	10	14	10	16	24	23	29	25	20	
B/O Demand							10												13			
Closing Stock		22	2	7	6	0	0	39	77	64	53	39	59	45	35	49	25	2	0	0	40	564 units @ £1 = £ 564
Lost Sales						10	38												14	8		70 units @ £10 = £ 700

Total stock-associated costs = £3,258

Figure 9.6 Simple ROQ/ROL worked example

the lead time relevant to future periods. In the completed tables the link lines show how 'goods on their way' shift from period to period according to the lead time.

ROQ is the Re-order Quantity. You specify what this shall be. It might be the same number throughout (e.g. '30' in simple Figure 9.6) or it could vary according to the latest information you have on demand and capacity (see note to Figure 9.7).

Cover If you place a new order, what have you available *before* that new order is delivered?

If Lead Time = 1 ... just Opening Stock
If Lead Time = 2 ... Opening Stock and (Transit-1)
If Lead Time = 3 ... Opening Stock and (Transit-1) + (Transit-2)

	0	1	2	3	4	5	6	7	8	9	10	11	12	13	14	15	16	17	18	19	20	
Let Forecast (F) = Previous Demand		20	18	20	25	31	26	28	21	22	13	11	14	10	14	10	16	24	23	29	25	
Lead Time (L)	1	2	2	2	3	3	2	2	1	1	1	1	2	2	2	3	3	3	2	1	1	12 orders @ £100 = £1,200
ROQ (see Note below)		(40)	(60)	(25)	0	(25)		(10)	(20)		(5)	(20)	(20)	(15)	(15)	(35)		(50)		(35)	(60)	
Let ROL = F × (L+1)		60	54	80	100	93	78	56	42	44	26	22	28	30	42	40	64	96	69	58		
Cover		40*	62	42*	77*	85*	85	57	36*	24*	31	20*	11*	21*	27*	35*	33*	50*	100	85		
Transit-2			(40)	(60)	(25)	(25)			(15)				(20)	(15)			(15)	(35)	(50)			
Transit-1		(40)		(60)	(60)		(20)		(20)				(15)	(15)	(35)	(35)						
Opening Stock	20	40	22	42	17	0	60	57	36	24	31	21	11	7	20	18	0	15	35	60		536 @ £1 = £ 536
Demand		18	20	25	31	26	28	21	22	13	11	20	14	10	16	24	23	29	25	20	40	
B/O Demand						7										1	3					
Closing Stock (CS)		22	2	17	0	0	32	36	14	11	20	6	1	7	0	3	0	0	0	10	40	221 @ £3 = £ 221
Lost Sales			7	33											2		3	26	14			85 @ £10 = £ 850

Total stock-associated costs = £2807

Note: Suppose that because of delivery constraints, the precise 'roq' has to be rounded up to an ROQ that is the next multiple of 5.
Then . . . .
If lead time has stayed unchanged, let roq = ROL − Cover
Add F to this figure if lead time has just increased
Subtract F from this figure if lead time has just decreased

Figure 9.7 More advanced ROQ/ROL worked example

ROL is the Re-order level. This is specified by you. If it is greater or equal to Cover an alarm bell rings (asterisk in the table) and you re-order. Again, it can be a set number (e.g. '60' in the simple table) or there can be a more complicated way of calculating it (see Figure 9.7 where it varies according to forecast demand and lead time).

Transit-2 When there is a lead time of 3, this is where an ROQ goes to in the period after it is ordered (see wavy lines in the worked tables). After another period passes (Transit-2) becomes (Transit-1).

Transit-1 When there is a lead time of 2, this is where ROQ goes to in the period after it is ordered (again see the wavy lines). After another period passes, (Transit-1) is added to Opening Stock.

Opening Stock This is a summation of these items from the previous period:

Closing Stock + (Transit − 1)+(ROQ where lead time=1)

Demand This has been generated externally. When deciding upon your decision rules you must not take advantage of these demand figures for the future. You must forecast from past items. At the beginning of a period you must make a re-order decision without knowing what the demand is for that period.

Closing Stock This is zero if Demand exceeds Opening Stock. Otherwise it is: (Opening Stock - Demand - B/O Demand). Closing Stock is added to next period's Opening Stock.

B/O Demand (Back-order Demand) and Lost Sales If Demand is greater than Opening Stock you have a stockout. Customers will either go to someone else or come back next period. If you had a stockout in the previous period as well, you can assume all your customers will go to another supplier. In this situation all your stockout is put in the Lost Sales row. If you did not have a stockout in the last period, some customers will wait and some will go elsewhere. Assume half of the stockout is put into Lost Sales and half into next period's B/O Demand.

Figure 9.6 shows a completed numerical example. Starting with an opening stock of 40 in period 1 it was possible to work through the table, period by period, calculating everything else.

After that, Figure 9.7 shows a more sophisticated way of calculating ROQ and ROL.

Because Figure 9.7 used more sophisticated rules for calculating ROQ and ROL, total stock costs are substantially lower than in Figure 9.6. Can you find an answer which is even better than that shown in Figure 9.7, but still finishing with a closing stock of 40 in period 20? (That was the amount of stock you started with, and you would need such an amount to carry on from period 21.) To ensure that you can achieve this level of closing stock, choose a suitable number for the last ROQ regardless of the standard rule for getting ROQ that applied otherwise.

Inventory Scheduling 2: Economic Order Quantity (EOQ)

Under certain restrictive assumptions it is possible to solve inventory problems by calculus. The commonest example is the EOQ formula in purchasing (Economic Order Quantity). This has the same format as the EBQ formula in manufacturing (Economic Batch Quantity):

$$\text{EOQ (or EBQ)} = \sqrt{\frac{2\,F\,D}{H}}$$

where F = fixed ordering or set-up cost independent of batch size
D = constant demand-rate per period
H = holding cost per item per period

Many texts explain the quite elementary derivation of this formula in great detail. We are not going to do this because we are going to argue later that EOQ should be abandoned or reformulated. However, here are some brief examples of EOQ being applied. As you read them, think about whether the application makes sense.

Example 1 A busy chip shop has a steady demand for three packets of chips per minute. When chips have been cooked there is a holding cost of 0.5p per minute per packet. When a batch is made, certain heating and oil costs are incurred, independent of the size of the batch. These costs come to 75p.

$$\text{EBQ} = \sqrt{\frac{2 \times 75 \times 3}{0.5}} = 30 \text{ packets of chips}$$

Example 2 A car showroom sells three new cars per week. To place an order for a new batch of cars to be delivered costs £30. There is a holding cost of £5 per week for any unsold cars kept in the showroom, made up of insurance, security costs, upkeep and obsolescence.

$$EOQ = \sqrt{\frac{2 \times 30 \times 3}{5}} = 6 \text{ cars}$$

Example 3 A chicken farmer needs to purchase 200 kilos of millet per month. He is some distance from the nearest grain store and the cost of driving there and picking up a bag of millet is £20 irrespective of the size of the load. When the millet is stored on the farmer's premises, damp and vermin cause it to deteriorate at a rate equivalent to 5p per kilo per month.

$$EOQ = \sqrt{\frac{2 \times 20 \times 200}{0.05}} = 400 \text{ kilos of millet}$$

Critique of EOQ Assumptions

EOQ highlights the balance that has to be maintained between fixed and variable costs − an important widespread feature in business. But EOQ should be regarded as no more than a *highlight*, because it assumes:

(i)   stable demand;
(ii)   a decision about one product is made independently of others;
(iii)   that the 'fixed order' and 'variable holding' costs are the dominant costs for batch decisions and that these costs can be estimated accurately;
(iv)   that choice is made over a continuum of alternatives;
(v)   that there are no leads and lags between decisions, deliveries, and payments;
(vi)   that minimising cost is equivalent to maximising profit;
(vii)   that there are no financial or physical constraints to the solution proposed;
(viii) that it is important to find a point-answer rather than a fuzzier range or approximate answer.

It is difficult to find a situation where all these conditions hold. To a certain extent expressions and variables can be added to the basic EOQ equation and an answer still found via calculus. This has been done where:

(i)   there is a period of time over which a manufactured batch is built up;

(ii)   the fixed batch or order cost applies to more than one product each with their own demand-rates and holding costs;

(iii)   there are various penalties for running out of stock before a new batch is made.

We will not dwell on these models because there are growing doubts about whether they are pointing inventory managers in the right direction. One reason is the dubious way in which costs are assembled for EOQ models. Another reason is that, using the same information, there is a better way of laying out and analysing these sort of problems.

A Cash-Flow Approach to EOQ-type Problems

Consider again Example 2, where a car showroom was selling three new cars a week. We found that the firm should order from the manufacturers a batch of six cars to be delivered over two weeks. Suppose each car costs £10,000 and sells for £11,000. If the buying and selling costs are paid on delivery, the cash-flow situation of the firm would be as shown in Table 9.1.

Table 9.1 Cash-flow situation of car showroom

| | | | | *Days (excluding Sundays)* | | | | |
	0	*2*	*4*	*6*	*8*	*10*	*12*	*14* ...
Purchase (£)	−60,000						−60,000	... etc.
Sales (£)		+11,000	+11,000	+11,000	+11,000	+11,000	+11,000	...
Order costs (£)	−30						−30	
Holding costs (£)	−30			−15			−30	

In this case as in many others, especially high-volume wholesaling and retailing businesses, the purchase/sales cash flows completely swamp the costs that EOQ focuses on. In such circumstances it is better to set out cash flows per period as above and analyse via a DCF (discounted cash flow) approach. This can cover many variants difficult to incorporate in EOQ, in particular those associated with varying lags between deliveries in payment.

In general the (more correct) DCF approach recommends significantly smaller optimal-batch sizes than the more widely known crude EOQ approaches. The difference becomes more noticeable the higher the interest rate. As many businesses have to operate with high costs of capital, often in excess of 20 per cent p.a. this is an important factor to bear in mind when devising an optimal-batch policy.

Work Scheduling 1: Machine Interference

Sometimes two or more machines are competing to use a scarce resource — such as a single man available to operate or adjust them, or a single material to be passed through them. By careful phasing of their operations, the damaging effect of one machine's interference on another's activity can be reduced.

For example in a plastics firm three men each have two injection-moulding machines under their control. The six machines are to make six products which have the characteristics shown in Table 9.2.

Table 9.2

	Products A B C D E F
Loading times (minutes) — man has to tend to machine	2 1 2 2 1 3
Running times (minutes) — machine works automatically	3 3 4 6 5 3

These six products are to be paired and given to the three men to make. Different pairings will give different patterns of operation. Consider, for example, the pairing of products A and B. If priority is to be given to making A, the best schedule is that shown in Figure 9.8.

During each regular operating cycle of 5 minutes, one unit of A and one unit of B is made. So the rate per hour is 12 for each product.

Now consider the best schedule if priority is given to making B, as shown in Figure 9.9.

Now there is a regular, repetitive operating cycle of 12 minutes. Within this period, A is made twice and B three times. So we have rates per hour of 10 for A and 15 for B.

Comparing the A-priority and B-priority schedules, we get the results shown in Table 9.3.

Table 9.3

	A-priority			B-priority		
	Prod. A Mach. I	Prod. B Mach. II	Man	Prod. A Mach. I	Prod. B. Mach. II	Man
Minutes utilised per hour	60	48	36	50	60	35
Items made per hour	12	12		10	15	

Crude statistics of machine utilisation should not solely determine your choice between such schedules. The pattern of the man's free time may

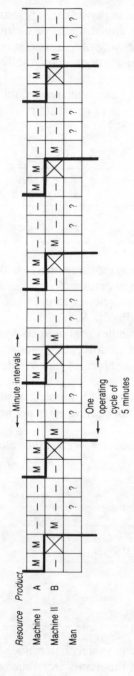

Figure 9.8 Machine interference — priority to product A

Key M Man is loading relevant machine
— Machine is running automatically without man's help
X Machine is idle, waiting for man to load it
? Shows the time when the man has no loading work — he may be able to fill in with other jobs, such as packing or shifting material or helping another worker, but most of this time will be wasted

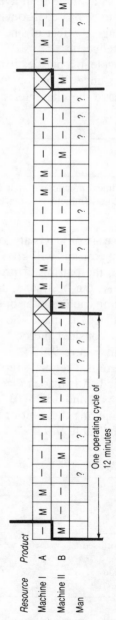

Figure 9.9 Machine interference — priority to product B

be different, influencing how much he can be used on other tasks. Note also that when you get round to pairing up C, D, E and F you are restricted in the levels of utilisation you can achieve because of your prior decision to pair up A and B.

Exercises

1 Use your own discretion to take two pairs from C, D, E and F for the remaining two men. Design optimal operating cycles letting each product have priority. Calculate utilisations and production rates in a similar fashion to the above.
2 Design an optimal pattern of operations for products A, B and C (in that order of priority) if run on three machines controlled by one man.

Set-up Times and Run Lengths with Machine Interference

So far, we have investigated how to co-ordinate machines to avoid simultaneously loading, each load taking only a few minutes. A more substantial delay to production occurs when a product is first assigned to a machine. Often, special jigs, dies or moulds have to be installed or the machine might have to be partially stripped and reassembled. This *set-up time* can take hours. With such a delay, once a product is on a machine it is good for it to stay there until a complete customer order is met.

Consider this problem. Eight products have the loading and automatic running times shown in Table 9.4.

Table 9.4

	Products							
	A	B	C	D	E	F	G	H
Loading times (minutes)	2	1	2	2	1	3	1	2
Automatic running (minutes)	3	3	4	6	5	3	4	2

Using our previous analysis, we could match each product against every other product to see the production rates for any pairing (see Figure 9.10). These production rates per hour provide a source of quick numerical estimates for the problem that follows.

Suppose you have to meet these rush orders for customer requirements.

A	B	C	D	E	F	G	H
60	60	100	60	60	120	120	120

If these are the rates for the first-priority products ↓

Then these are the rates possible for second-priority product ↓

Second-priority products

			A	B	C	D	E	F	G	H
A	12		A		12	8	6	9	6	12	12
B	15	*First-*	B	10		7.5	7.5	10	7.5	11.3	15
C	10	*priority*	C	10	10		6.7	10	10	10	10
D	7.5	*products*	D	7.5	15	7.5		7.5	7.5	11.3	15
E	10		E	10	15	10	6.7		10	10	10
F	10		F	10	15	10	10	5		10	10
G	12		G	12	12	9	6	9.6	8		12
H	15		H	7.5	15	7.5	7.5	7.5	0	10	

Figure 9.10

Two operators each have a pair of machines to help meet this order. When each product is put on a machine there is a two-hour delay whilst the machine is set up. A third man, a skilled craftsman, has to do this. As he is the only person available, two machines cannot be set up simultaneously.

Figure 9.11 shows an answer that takes 28 hours.

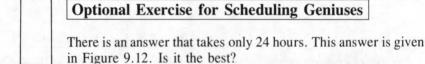

| **Optional Exercise for Scheduling Geniuses** |

There is an answer that takes only 24 hours. This answer is given in Figure 9.12. Is it the best?

Further extensions to the machine-interference problem   Even with a skilled workforce it is difficult to match planned output with actual. Quick shuffling of resources is necessary to meet material shortage, absenteeism or machine breakdown. With heavily used machines there is a gradual deterioration in tolerances which requires continual monitoring of performance and statistical quality control. Many machines are affected by temperature or humidity and necessitate difficult adjustments to working conditions. There has been a general move towards automatically loaded machines which are only shut down for repair or a major resetting. Thus schedulers are

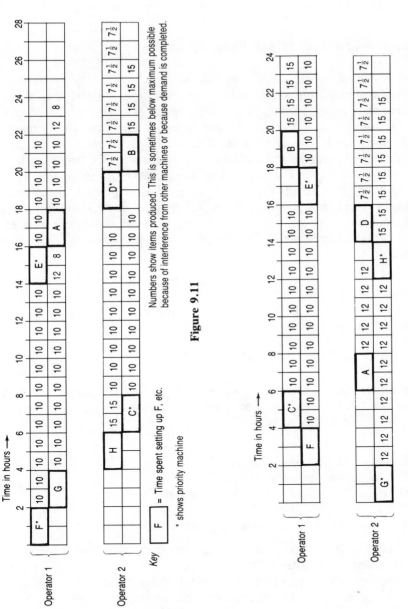

Figure 9.11

Numbers show items produced. This is sometimes below maximum possible because of interference from other machines or because demand is completed.

Key   [F] = Time spent setting up F, etc.

* shows priority machine

Figure 9.12 'Optional exercise for scheduling geniuses': Best answer?

becoming more concerned with the Figure 9.11 situation than the earlier machine-interference examples. One new, computer-related technique called OPT has claimed success at tackling complex problems of this type.

Work Scheduling 2: Job Shop Scheduling

Job shops make work to order, one customer's job needing to call on many processes and machines. (Note, in this context, 'job' is always a customer order, never a task.) Often, management specifies a manufacturing route, i.e. a sequence of operations, that the customer's job must pass through. This sequence is usually a technical necessity: sometimes, by having a sequence, you help ensure that no task is overlooked. Occasionally there is some flexibility in the sequence of operations that can be followed.

Although we usually think of job shop scheduling in a manufacturing context, there are a variety of applications elsewhere in operations management, e.g. surgical operations, repair work, education modules or catering arrangements. The distinguishing features of the job shop situation are:

(i)   every new time period brings a new, unique set of customer jobs to handle;

(ii)   the customer jobs have to be sequenced through a complex set of processes.

Heuristic Job Shop Scheduling

Car-repair garages are classic examples of job shops, especially garages with specialist mechanics. For example, suppose mechanics specialise within one of these functions:

A Auto-electrical work
B Bodywork and passenger interiors
C Chassis and suspension
D Drive units: clutch, gearing, crankshafts
E Engine and ancillaries
F Fixed replacements: exhaust, brakes, tyres

To keep the illustration simple, we assume that a department can work on only one car at a time.

Figure 9.13 shows all major jobs booked in for repair on a particular day. Along any row is the sequence of operations that a particular customer job must go through. Each box-section represents an hour's work.

Suppose S has to be finished by 4 p.m., Q by 5 p.m. and the rest by 6 p.m. Figure 9.14 gives a schedule that never loads a department with more than one car simultaneously.

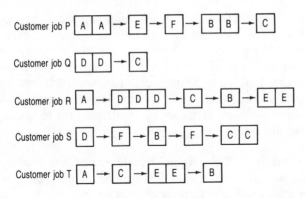

Figure 9.13

Customer job	9	10	11	12	1	2	3	4	5	6
Customer job P			A	A	E	F	B	B	C	
Customer job Q						D	D	C		
Customer job R	A	D	D	D	C	B		E	E	
Customer job S	D		F	B	F	C	C			
Customer job T		A	C			E	E		B	

(a) Primary schedule, highlighting job sequences over hours of work, 9 a.m. to 6 p.m.

Exactly the same schedule can be drawn up in another way:

	9	10	11	12	1	2	3	4	5	6
Repair Dept A	R	T	P	P						
Repair Dept B				S		R	P	P	T	
Repair Dept C			T		R	S	S	Q	P	
Repair Dept D	S	R	R	R		Q	Q			
Repair Dept E					P	T	T	R	R	
Repair Dept F			S		S	P				

(b) Dual schedule, highlighting the loading of departments from 9 a.m. to 6 p.m.

Figure 9.14

The lower schedule in Figure 9.14 is a 'dual schedule'. Jobs are allocated to departments exactly as before, but now all of a department's work appears along the same row, labelled this time as its customer job. This format highlights manpower scheduling. For example, looking at work done between 12 noon and 2 p.m. you can see that three departments take a lunch break from 12 to 1, the other three departments from 1 to 2, giving reasonable cover for emergencies.

Because of gaps in the schedule this might appear to be a pretty slack system. Not so. (Could you get all work finished by 5 p.m., even by getting the mechanics to forgo their lunch hour?) Also, in this example a gap does not mean that a mechanic is idle. Good scheduling provides a bank of other work which can be done at leisure (e.g. cars owned by the repair shop can be stripped, cannibalised or prepared for second-hand sale). Also, 'idle' mechanics can help busy departments by driving off to spares shops to get parts that are needed.

Slotting in extra jobs The original schedule considered only major jobs requiring the attention of several departments. There is room to slot in a few minor jobs, especially those dealt with by only one department (e.g., along the F-row, fitting a new exhaust or replacing brake pads). But trouble can occur if a late minor job turns up and is given priority. For example, what would happen if you fitted a minor job (e.g. a clutch adjustment) into D's morning schedule arguing 'It'll only take us an hour to do, and we'll have plenty of spare time to finish our work in the afternoon'?

Department D may have spare time, but other departments dependent on D will have all their work put back. So, one little addition can cause major havoc elsewhere.

Exercise

Use the same layouts as in the previous example but with an extra row for customer U and two extra columns in case you have to work until 7 or 8 p.m. For the data in Figure 9.15 find

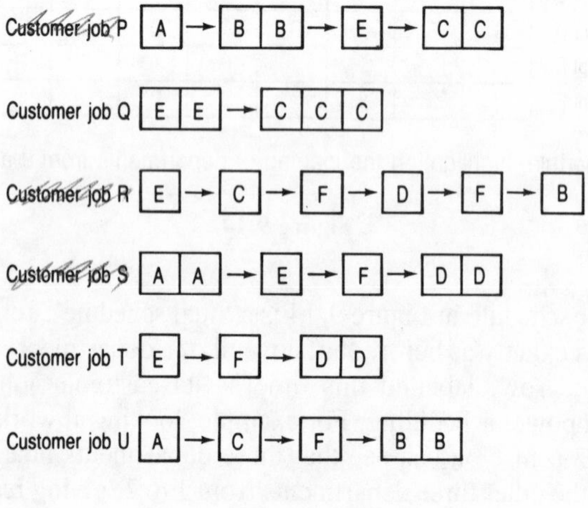

Customer job P A → B B → E → C C

Customer job Q E E → C C C

Customer job R E → C → F → D → F → B

Customer job S A A → E → F → D D

Customer job T E → F → D D

Customer job U A → C → F → B B

Figure 9.15

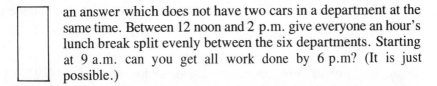

an answer which does not have two cars in a department at the same time. Between 12 noon and 2 p.m. give everyone an hour's lunch break split evenly between the six departments. Starting at 9 a.m. can you get all work done by 6 p.m? (It is just possible.)

The effect of local priority rules on an overall schedule   Good scheduling pays careful attention to *interdependencies*. Sometimes such a schedule is overruled on the shop floor by expediters, who want to get more work through a particular point or for a particular customer. Also, when there is a queue of work waiting at a process, items are sometimes taken from the queue according to certain *priority rules*, and these rules can ruin a good tight schedule.

Priority rules commonly used involve giving priority to the job:

(i)   that has been waiting longest:
(ii)   with shortest time to completion;
(iii)   with longest time to completion;
(iv)   needed earliest;
(v)   with the least slack time left;
(vi)   with the most remaining different types of operation;
(vii)   with the lowest critical ratio (where critical ratio = time to completion/periods of work left to do).

If any of these rules were applied to the example in Figure 9.14 they would make matters worse. For example:

Rules (i), (ii) and (iv) would get D working on Q at 10 a.m.
Rules (iii), (v), (vi) and (vii) would get A working on P at 10 a.m.

For either of these happenings, the garage cannot get its work done, even cutting into the mechanics' lunch breaks. So this is a good example of where *local* priority rules should be avoided.

Work Scheduling 3: Just-In-Time Schedules

Sometimes the manufacturing route taken by all customer jobs is very nearly the same. For example, in the manufacture of cutlery, all spoons and forks are made via this sequence of operations:

(i)   blanking (stamping out flat shapes from thin sheets of metal);
(ii)   pressing (bending the shapes);
(iii)   edging (trimming, rounding and pointing the shapes);
(iv)   cleaning (abrading and polishing);
(v)   finishing (trademark etching and packing).

But each customer job will have its own special times needed to complete each operation.

One further difference in standard route shops lies on the marketing side. Their customers are more likely to allow flexibility in the size and timing of an order. For example, a customer having agreed for 12,000 items to be delivered during the next year, the supplier has some discretion as to whether this is 1,000 a month or (say) 3,000 a quarter. If a fair proportion of orders are like this, then orders do not arrive and depart in such clumps (as at the car-repair job shop). In such circumstances it is worth considering the *Sandman Rule,* to get a *Just-In-Time* (JIT) schedule: 'When a job starts at the first operation, there must be no break in work until it is finished.'

For example, you get production schedules like the one shown in two forms in Figure 9.16.

If you look at the primary schedule, you will see that there are no gaps where material would be lying around waiting to be processed. The only work in progress is on machines.

Against this efficiency gain is the potentially idle machine time revealed in the dual schedule. As we are dealing with steady arrival and take-off of work, the spaces in the bottom left and top right can be filled up with earlier and later orders. But the spaces in the centre, between the thick lines, are harder to fill in. Some of this could be subcontract work for other manufacturers, non-urgent items, or making for stock. But, on the

Customer's job J	1	1	2	2	2	3	4	5	5											
Customer's job K				1	2	2	3	3	4	4	4	5								
Customer's job L							1	1	2	2	3	4	5	5	5					
Customer's job M										1	2	3	3	4	4	5				
Customer's job N												1	2	2	2	3	4	4	5	

(a) Primary, customer-layered schedule

1. Blanking	J	J			K			L	L		M	N						Later jobs starting
2. Pressing		J	J	J	K	K			L	L	M	N	N	N				
3. Edging				J		K	K			L	M	M		N				
4. Cleaning	Earlier jobs finishing				J		K	K	K	L			M	M	N	N		
5. Finishing					J	J			K	L	L	L	M		N			

(b) Dual, resource-layered schedule

Note: Numbers 1,2, etc. in the Primary schedule refer to blanking, pressing, etc.

Figure 9.16

whole, such gaps in the schedule are not likely to be regarded kindly by the operatives, if they are on piecework. It is no good telling them that the organisation as a whole benefits if they are sometimes idle. Pieceworkers much prefer to see a permanent queue of work waiting to be done whether they are lowly paid sewing machinists or highly paid hospital consultants. So a prime requirement for establishing a Just-In-Time scheduling system is the abandonment of *individual* piecework payment systems.

Apart from reducing material inventories there are other advantages of a Just-In-Time system. If you do not send material non-stop through a set of processes it tends to get put on one side and '*squirreled away*', *stolen, misrouted* or *forgotton about.*

Also, without the Just-In-Time discipline there is a temptation to attack the scheduling problem by *front-end overloading* or a *Just-In-Case* system. More material than necessary is pushed through the earlier processes with the vague intention of ensuring that the remaining processes are kept busy, even allowing for material getting lost and muddled up. Such a system gets even more muddled and encourages workers to do their own thing, rather than take note of the schedule.

Exercise

In the previous illustration there were 18 spaces between the thick lines of the dual resource schedule. Suppose you take the present sequence of customers (J K L M N) and change it, e.g. to N M L K J among other possibilities. Can you find a solution where there are only 16 spaces between the heavy lines?

Work Scheduling 4: Line Balancing

In Figure 9.17, each labelled box is a *job* to be done on an assembly line. The number in the box is the *job element* (in seconds) which tells you how long it takes to complete one job before passing it on down the line. The arrows show you how work is passed on from one job to the next. Several sub-assembly lines merge, giving one completed product (a burglar alarm) after job x has been done. If you have six workers how should they divide the 24 jobs between them?

If each worker works 450 minutes a day, that equals 27,000 seconds per day. Multiplying by six for the six workers means you have 162,000 seconds of work available.

There are 24 jobs, and if you added up the job elements of a, b, c, etc. you would get $20 + 20 + 30$, etc. — which sums up to 600 seconds to make one burglar alarm.

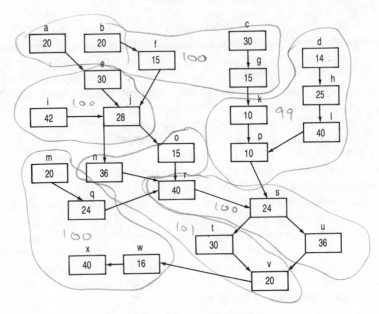

Figure 9.17 Jobs on an assembly line

If you have 162,000 seconds available and it takes 600 seconds to make one burglar alarm then, if you balance your line perfectly, you should be able to make 162,000/600 = 270 burglar alarms per day.

Making 270 burglar alarms in a 450-minute working day means that one burglar alarm is being completed every 100 seconds. This figure of 100 seconds is known as the *control cycle* of the assembly line.

In elementary line balancing (like here) it is the practice to give a worker a rota of jobs, so that his or her *personal cycle* (before repetition) equals the control cycle. It is also good practice to give the worker a group of jobs that are geographically adjacent. The group of jobs assigned to one worker is known as a *work station*.

Ideally, every worker's personal cycle should be the same. In practice it is rarely possible to get clusters of jobs whose times all sum up exactly to (say) 100 seconds. So one looks for a set of worker assignments where everyone's personal cycle is within a fairly narrow range.

Exercise

Can you assign jobs to six workers so that each worker's personal cycle lies within an acceptably narrow range, 95 to 104 seconds?

Time Losses for Job Switching

Is it practicable to expect no delay when an assembly worker switches from one job (using a certain location, posture or material) to another? Zero delay is likely only if the next job follows in a natural sequence (e.g. is next down the line on a flow chart). If this is not so, let us assume a 15-second delay.

With this new assumption you will need more than six workers to cover all 24 jobs within the 100-second control cycle. One such example is shown in Figure 9.18.

This example assumes that 15 seconds are lost when switching to a job that does not flow from the last job. Jobs are assigned to eight workers, every worker's personal cycle being less than 100.

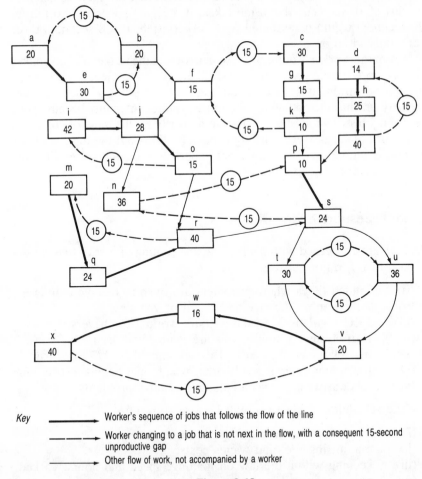

Key   ──────▶   Worker's sequence of jobs that follows the flow of the line

         ─ ─ ─ ─▶   Worker changing to a job that is not next in the flow, with a consequent 15-second unproductive gap

         ──────▶   Other flow of work, not accompanied by a worker

Figure 9.18

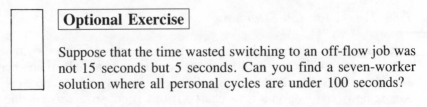

Optional Exercise

Suppose that the time wasted switching to an off-flow job was not 15 seconds but 5 seconds. Can you find a seven-worker solution where all personal cycles are under 100 seconds?

High-intensity Assembly Lines

Suppose that the assembly line that we have been using as an example was required to make 2,700 rather than 270 burglar alarms a day. This could be achieved by employing more workers (66 to be precise) and dropping the control cycle from 100 to 10 seconds. Now, workers are allocated to only one job or a part of one — in fact for each 10 seconds (or part of 10 seconds) that a job takes, it receives a worker. So job 'a' (20 seconds) would be assigned two workers, job 'j' (28 seconds) three workers, and so on.

From the worker's point of view, narrowing the range of tasks makes the job more boring and it really needs an incentive piecework scheme to keep up productivity. From the management point of view a high-intensity line has the potential to be more productive mainly because time lost from job switching is avoided and only partly for the more often quoted reason of greater dexterity through specialisation. But the high-intensity system requires greater management expertise in balancing the line and keeping material flowing through it.

Road Transport Scheduling

Here we are concerned with the loading and routing of lorries to a variety of customers. Major constraints are:

(i)   limited times when customers are open to receive deliveries;
(ii)   limitation on the size and speed of vehicles;
(iii)   EEC regulations on daily hours worked by drivers;
(iv)   restrictions on how lorries are loaded and secured;
(v)   the relatively high cost of diesel since the 1973 oil crisis;
(vi)   traffic congestion, roadworks, weight and height restrictions;
(vii)   random weather, accidents and security problems.

The scheduler's objectives will be a mixture of:

(i)   rapid response to customer requests;
(ii)   minimising fuel and wages costs;
(iii)   keeping within the law on loading, speed and hours worked;
(iv)   giving a fair allocation of work to drivers.

Types of Scheduling Problem

Basically these can be divided into part drops and full drops.

(1) *Part drops* are where the depot loads a vehicle with goods for several customers (classically a parcels service). Usually the vehicle does a circular tour, returning to the depot. In an urban conurbation the vehicle usually returns at the end of the day. For deliveries throughout the United Kingdom there may be two or three overnight stops. The part-drop situation is similar to that of the travelling sales representative: he or she will manage greater speeds, but will be subject to different types of delay when trying to meet clients.

(2) *Full drops* are where the entire lorry's capacity is used for one customer's load. Full drops may be split into *short-haul* deliveries, such as earth removed by building contractors, and *long-haul* deliveries which may involve travelling to the other side of Europe or even Saudi Arabia. In general, full drops involve heavier vehicles with slower speeds and more stringent restrictions on routes used and hours driven.

The peculiar problems facing a transport schedule are best demonstrated by reference to a map. Without reading further, what would be your reaction to solving Exercises 1 to 3 below, which refer to Figure 9.19?

Exercises

1. *One vehicle has the capacity to meet all the customers' requirements*
Starting from the depot, one vehicle must make a drop at every circled customer on the map and return to the triangle. Using timings of 5 minutes per motorway section, 10 minutes per other road and 10 minutes per 'drop', find the route which takes the minimum time. (*Hint*: 9½ hours would be a good result.)

2. *Two vehicles have the capacity to meet all the customers' requirements*
Starting from the depot, can you schedule two lorries to deliver to all customers, both lorries returning to base in 5 hours or less? Again use timings of 5 minutes per motorway section, 10 minutes per other road and 10 minutes per 'drop'.

3. *Full loads handled by several vehicles doing several round trips*
Use the same times as above. Now you have four lorries, all of which must have completed their work and returned to the depot in 7 hours. Customers at the 23 circle points each want

10 road
1 num
10 load

350 .
355 .
230
6) 585 .
6) 58.8

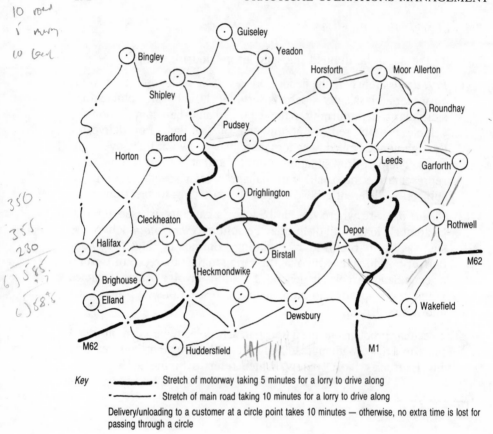

Key   ·━━━━· Stretch of motorway taking 5 minutes for a lorry to drive along
       ·────· Stretch of main road taking 10 minutes for a lorry to drive along
Delivery/unloading to a customer at a circle point takes 10 minutes — otherwise, no extra time is lost for passing through a circle

Figure 9.19 Network of trunk roads in the West Yorkshire conurbation

a full lorry load, so lorries will have to make several trips. The lorries start the day fully loaded. When a lorry returns to the depot it cannot be loaded at the same time as one of the other three lorries. Reloading at the depot takes 10 minutes.

Hint for Finding an Answer to Exercise 1 (one complete circuit of part drops)

Finding a loop through a complete set of points has been christened the 'Travelling Salesman Problem' (TSP). The problem has received an inordinate amount of attention from mathematicians compared with that given to other vehicle-scheduling problems. An appreciation of TSP must

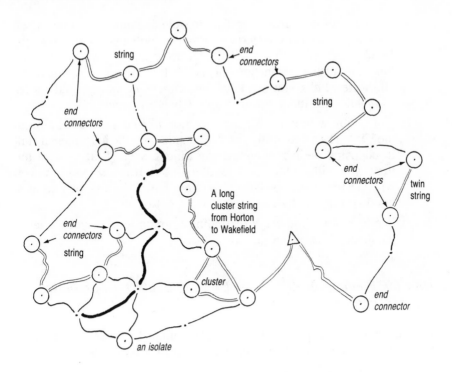

Key .≈≈· Stretches joining circles equal to or less than the prime connecting time of 10 minutes

.——· Other roads   }
——   Motorways   } remaining routes after 'doctoring'

Figure 9.20

focus on the map rather than the mathematics. Figure 9.20 shows a doctored map which makes the discovery of the optimal solution understandable.

These were the stages used to get from the original to this doctored map:

(1) Pay particular attention to all connections that are equal to or less than a certain time that you specify. Score these connections in with double lines and call them *prime connections*. In our example we have used 10 minutes as the prime connecting time.

(2) With reference solely to double-line links, identify *clusters* and *strings* (with end connectors). The definitions of these terms should be self explanatory if you look at Figure 9.20. An *isolate* is any circle not on a double-line string.

(3) Eliminate all roads which are not on the shortest route between any

end connector, cluster member or isolate. Sometimes there is an obvious link-up between strings (as in the north and east of our map). In this case you can confine yourself to an end connector's nearest links and further eliminations can be made. But be sure you maintain all shortest links between other *end connectors, isolates* and *cluster members* (i.e. those of the map's labels in italics).

(4) You are now in a much better position to find a good solution to the TSP. The worth of this method depends on the judgemental skill in choosing the prime connecting time at stage 1. If it is set too high, you will get too many 'double links'. If it is set too low, you will get too many 'isolates'. In either case, the task of finding a good solution is harder.

(5) We leave the final stage of finding a grand loop to you. It takes 9½ hours (answer on p.197).

Hint for Finding an Answer to Exercise 2 (part drops shared between two lorries)

Use the simplified map of Figure 9.20. The optimal answer has one lorry taking 290 minutes, the other 300 minutes (answer on p. 197).

Solution to Exercise 3 (full loads delivery)

(1) In this problem there is no need to consider 'between customer' routes as drivers spend all their time going either from depot to a customer or from customer back to depot. So work out shortest distance from depot to each customer and eliminate every other route not used.

(2) For each customer, calculate the time for an out-and-back trip, including the 10-minute unloading at the customer and the 10-minute loading at the depot. These round-trip times are put above each customer circle in Figure 9.21.

(3) Add up all the out-and-back times (= 1,720). Divide by four to get 430 minutes, which, if you can give it to each lorry, is the most even result.

Group customers under each lorry so the out-and-back timings sum to 430, as, for example, in Table 9.5. On the final return to the depot there is no need to include the 10-minute 'loading time for next customer', so all drivers can finish by 420 minutes rather than 430.

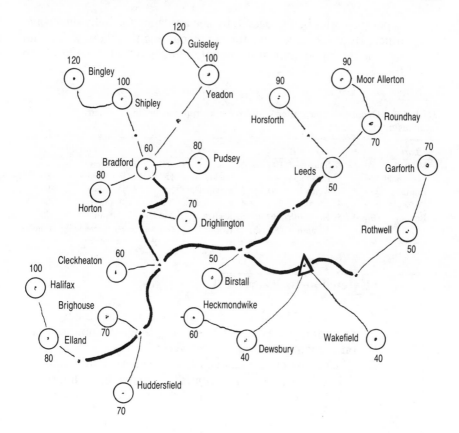

Figure 9.21

(4) Whilst the lorries are ferrying backwards and forwards between customers, you have to ensure that the depot is not asked to load two lorries at the same time. If lorries make deliveries in the order listed above, you can work out the time when a lorry leaves the

Table 9.5 Out-and-back timings (minutes)

Lorry A		Lorry B		Lorry C		Lorry D	
1. Moor A	90	1. Shipley	100	1. Elland	80	1. Guiseley	120
2. Wakefield	40	2. Dewsbury	40	2. Huddersfield	70	2. Bradford	60
3. Halifax	100	3. Birstall	50	3. Brighouse	70	3. Dewsbury	70
4. Pudsey	80	4. Leeds	50	4. Cleckheaton	60	4. Rothwell	50
5. Bingley	120	5. Horsforth	90	5. Roundhay	70	5. Garforth	70
		6. Yeadon	100	6. Horton	80	6. Heckmondwike	60
	430		430		430		430

depot (just after being loaded) by accumulating the individual route times. By inspecting these times you can see that there will be no overlap during loading at the depot, and a good schedule has been found.

Table 9.6 Departure times after completing a drop and being reloaded (minutes after start)

Lorry A			Lorry B			Lorry C			Lorry D		
1. Moor A	90		1. Shipley	100		1. Elland	80		1. Guiseley	120	
2. Wakefield	130		2. Dewsbury	140		2. Huddersfield	150		2. Bradford	180	
3. Halifax	230		3. Birstall	190		3. Brighouse	220		3. Dewsbury	250	
4. Pudsey	310		4. Leeds	240		4. Cleckheaton	280		4. Rothwell	300	
5. Bingley	(Finish)		5. Horsforth	330		5. Roundhay	350		5. Garforth	370	
			6. Yeadon	(Finish)		6. Horton	(Finish)		6. Heckmondwike	(Finish)	

Extension to Exercise 1

1. If you could omit deliveries to three of your 23 customers, what route between any remaining 20 would minimise time on a complete circuit of deliveries?
2. What is the circuit that can cover the maximum number of deliveries in under two hours? ... under three hours? ... (*Hint*: You can cover ten and thirteen deliveries for these two cases.)

Extension to Exercise 2

1. In Exercise 2, from the existing depot it is just possible for two lorries to cover all customers and return to base in 5 hours. Is there another motorway junction that would be a better site for a depot, in the sense that two lorries could cover all customers in less than 5 hours?
2. If instead of the existing depot you could locate two depots at different junction points, with one vehicle operating from each, where would these depots be to minimise total circuit time? (Only use junction points which are not within customer circles for depots.)

Concluding Comments on Transport Scheduling

We hope this section has given you some feel for the skills of the transport scheduler. We have barely touched upon some of the other problems —

balancing loads, handling varying customer priorities, arranging subcontractors and taking on return loads. All this is on a vaster scale than we have space for in this book. The mathematical nature of these problems is such that *decisions* are best made by human skill and judgement, reserving computers to provide the *decision-support system* (listing and filing data and doing the 'What if?' calculations for alternative solutions proposed by humans). Now that we have touched on the stresses and complexity facing the transport scheduler, you should be in a better position to appreciate the Harry Britton case mentioned earlier in the book (pp. 74–77).

Answer to Exercise 1

This is the best anticlockwise route (arrival times are bracketed in minutes after starting):

Wakefield (10), Rothwell (40), Garforth (60), Leeds (90), Roundhay (110), Moor Allerton (130), Horsforth (150), Yeadon (180), Guiseley (200), Shipley (220), Bingley (240), Bradford (280), Horton (300), Halifax (330), Elland (350), Brighouse (370), Cleckheaton (390), Pudsey (430), Drighlington (450), Birstall (470), Heckmondwike (490), Huddersfield (520), Dewsbury (550), Depot (570).

Answer to Exercise 2

Lorry A Dewsbury, Huddersfield, Heckmondwike, Birstall, Drighlington, Pudsey, Bradford, Horton, Halifax, Elland, Brighouse, Cleckheaton, Depot. 290 minutes.

Lorry B Wakefield, Rothwell, Garforth, Leeds, Roundhay, Moor Allerton, Horsforth, Yeadon, Guiseley, Shipley, Bingley, Depot. 300 minutes.

Total Scheduling Systems 1: MRP

Introduction

MRP-1 (Materials Requirement Planning) is an American computer-based technique introduced in the mid-1970s. Its objective is to integrate scheduling and inventory-management functions, particularly where there is much sub-assembly work with various lead-times. Initially used in the electronics industry, it has been successfully tried in the automobile-assembly, clothing and furniture industries, amongst others. Recently,

MRP-1 has been enhanced by MRP-2 (Manufacturing Resources Planning) which goes beyond immediate scheduling to cover the complete operating strategy, information and control system of a company.

To a certain extent MRP has been replaced as the fashionable technique by JIT (Just-In-Time). Whereas Just-In-Time is a management philosophy which can be introduced piecemeal, MRP demands an all-or-nothing commitment by management to invest in an integrated computer package, to collect special information that is needed by that package, and to have that package's instructions obeyed. This was possible in the well-organised, high-tech firms like IBM which pioneered the technique. But firms with little experience of formalised planning had great difficulty in understanding, installing and implementing expensive MRP systems. This is a pity. There are some very simple, very convenient little sub-procedures in MRP that operating managers should be aware of even if they don't want to install an all-singing, all-dancing MRP computer package. So we are going to concentrate on explaining some bits and pieces of MRP rather than investigating a full-blown system.

The Product Structure Tree

This adds certain numerical data to the 'Gozinto Chart' (see Chapter 7). An augmented Gozinto Chart for a confectionery manufacturer is shown in Figure 9.22.

The coefficients placed against the arrows enable you to find out the quantities of ingredients to make any product. For example if you want to make 80 units of K, you will need $(0.7) \times 80$ of BM and $(0.3) \times 80$ of CM. But MRP is concerned with not only the quantities of raw materials but also the *time* when they should be prepared and passed on. For this reason, every operation has a lead time affixed to it.

Levelling

There is a certain principle of dynamic programming which greatly helps untangle complex situations: 'work backwards from where you want to be, rather than work forwards from where you are at the moment'.

Levelling is a preliminary to this dynamic programming principle. In the confectionery example, finished products (by definition) have arrows only going into them. Put all these at Level 0. Of the remaining boxes, put those at Level 1 that have arrows going only to Level 0. And of the remaining boxes, put those at Level 2 that have arrows going only to Level 1 or less. The general rule should be obvious for a many-levelled system.

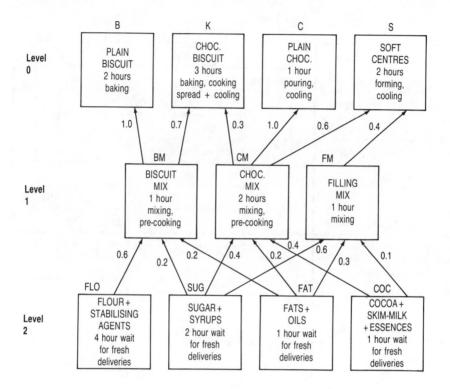

Figure 9.22 Augmented Gozinto Chart for confectionery manufacturer

The purpose of levelling is to disentangle the element of derived demand. Many businesses are making things not directly for their customers but for other departments in their organisation, or for a sub-assembly that is going to be embodied in a final product. By working backwards from levels 0, 1, 2, etc. you avoid your calculations of derived demand going round in circles.

Exploding

Refer to Figure 9.23. Starting with the known demand, at a known time for Level 0 products, the lead times (lags) and coefficients in the product structure tree are used to work out how much of, and when, Level 1 products should be made. This is then repeated to find Level 2, etc.

Originally, the table contained just circled numbers: finished product requirements. These requirements were then lagged to find out when you needed to start manufacturing them (the ENTER rows in the Level 0 part

Time in hours

Level			1	2	3	4	5	6	7	8	9	10	11	12	13
0	B	LEAVE				(150)	(150)	(100)	(50)			(100)	(150)	(150)	(100)
		LEAVE, lagged 2 = ENTER		150	150	100	50			100	150	150	100		
	K	LEAVE						(60)	(100)	(120)	(120)				
		LEAVE, lagged 3 = ENTER			60	100	120	120							
	C	LEAVE				(100)	(150)	(100)	(50)						
		LEAVE, lagged 1 = ENTER			100	150	100	50							
	S	LEAVE										(40)	(80)	(100)	(100)
		LEAVE, lagged 2 = ENTER								40	80	100	100		
1	BM	LEAVES { = B		150	150	100	50			100	150	150	100		
		= 0.7K			42	70	84	84							
		LEAVES, lagged 1 = ENTER	150	192	170	134	84		100	150	150	100			
	CM	= 0.3K LEAVES {			18	30	36	36							
		= C			100	150	100	50							
		= 0.6S								24	48	60	60		
		LEAVES, Lagged 2 = ENTER	118	180	136	86		24	48	60	60				
	FM	= 0.4S LEAVE								16	32	40	40		
		LEAVES, lagged 1 = ENTER							16	32	40	40			

Recap on the order in which calculations are carried out:
(i) Level 0's 'ENTERS'
(ii) Level 1's 'LEAVES'
(iii) Level 1's 'ENTERS'

Figure 9.23 Exploding from Level 0 to Level 1

of the table). Then via the ingredient coefficients it was found out what needed to be available at Level 1 LEAVE rows. Then via the lag-factor it was discovered when manufacturing needed to start (ENTER rows at Level 1).

Exercise

Extend Figure 9.23 down to Level 2 using the information in Figure 9.22.

Further MRP-related Techniques

One big advantage of MRP is that it has been able to incorporate clever practices employed in other areas of scheduling:

(1) *Dynamic lot-sizes*   This uses the dynamic programming 'working backwards' principle to work out best batch sizes.
(2) *Discounted cash flows*   This has been illustrated in the EOQ section.
(3) *Pegging*   Via computer graphics, this shows what happens when a planned schedule suffers disruptions. It owes its name to the efforts of early Scientific Management pioneers to trace disruptions by moving coloured cards on a pegboard. This is illustrated in the Job Shop Scheduling section.

One big disadvantage of MRP is the sometimes awkward jargon and method of calculation employed. For example, MRP's 'netting' (phasing deliveries to take account of lead time) is highlighted much more clearly in ROQ/ROL (see Figures 9.6 and 9.7) than can be shown in MRP.

Summary and Evaluation of MRP

The potential advantages of installing MRP are:

(1) It sets up an integrated, standardised data base of information.
(2) It cuts stock levels and improves delivery performance by a correct handling of interdependencies and lead times.
(3) It can accommodate a variety of other scheduling techniques within its general framework.
(4) When MRP becomes operational, its *execution modules* perform all the number crunching previously performed by human schedulers. This releases them either to improve the quality of the permanent embedded information used, or to tackle problems of diagnosis and implementation.

The potential disadvantages of MRP are:
(1) The cost of the computer package and hardware and systems changes.
(2) The cost of employing consultants to get MRP operational.
(3) Difficulties in educating and persuading the workforce to conform to MRP procedures.

Total Scheduling Systems 2: Continuous Processing

In the oil and chemical industry, plants run for 24 hours a day, month after month, with only occasional shutdowns for repair. Where there is a complex group of continuously running plant, as at an oil refinery, special scheduling problems arise. Special care has to be taken to synchronise plant operations. Properly, this is the province of the chemical and control engineer. But quite good approximate solutions can be generated by linear programming (LP). Depending on the size of the refinery, a full linear programme will consist of between 500 and 5,000 constraints. We have constructed a simplified refinery problem with just under 50 constraints. It is possible to get quick hand solutions to this problem. This is a useful exercise to carry out prior to formulating it as an LP and feeding into a computer package to get a solution. A little practice with hand solutions reduces formulation errors and black-box mentality.

Exercise

Refer to Figure 9.24.

Crude oil is fed into Distillation on the left-hand side. After passing through various pipelines (arrows), tanks (circles) and processing plant (boxes), it emerges as finished products on the right-hand side of the diagram. You are free to choose which of ten crude oils to feed into Distillation and can take either a single crude oil or a mixture of these. Table 9.7 shows what happens when 1 unit of each type of crude oil is fed through Distillation.

Apart from Distillation, every other plant has only one input feeding into it. Output from any of these plants is expressed as a decimal fraction of the relevant input. These decimal fractions are placed against the output pipelines in Figure 9.24. Because of volume changes, total yields from various chemical processes do not always sum to 1.0, e.g. thermal cracking converts 1 unit of reduced crude into 0.7 units of untreated thermal gasoline and 0.5 units of black fuel oils.

Usually, total tank input and total tank output should balance. But if you find it impossible to meet a blending requirement, assume you can drain oil to waste, either at a tank or anywhere else in the system.

Getting a first feasible answer   Choose any combination of crude oils which come to 1,000 units, Feed these 1,000 units into Distillation and using the yields at Distillation and subsequent plants, work out the quantities of finished products. Try to meet all the blending requirements without having to send too much oil to waste. Keep things simple by rounding down to avoid decimal fractions of a unit.

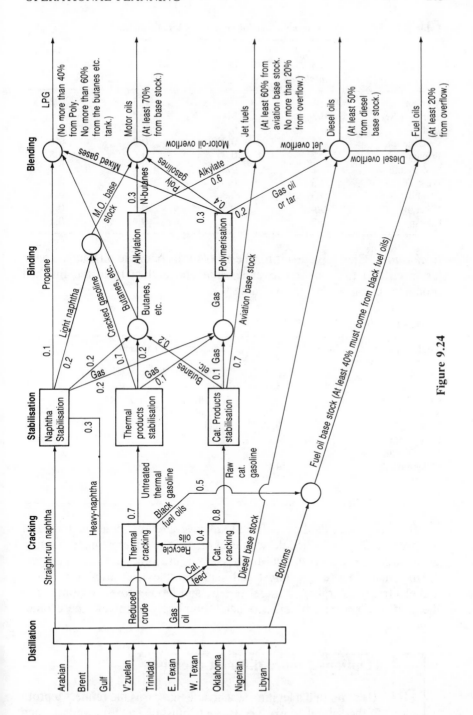

Figure 9.24

Table 9.7 How 1 unit of crude-oil input splits up after distillation

	Straight-run naphtha	Reduced crude	Gas oil	Bottoms
Arabian	0.1	0.4	0.3	0.2
Brent (N.Sea)	0.3	0.4	0.2	0.1
Gulf	0.3	0.2	0.2	0.3
Venezuelan	0.1	0.2	0.2	0.5
Trinidad	0.2	0.3	0	0.5
East Texan	0.2	0.3	0.2	0.3
West Texan	0.3	0.3	0.2	0.2
Oklahoma	0.3	0.3	0.1	0.3
Nigerian	0.4	0.1	0.1	0.4
Libyan	0.2	0.3	0.4	0.1

Evaluation Charge yourself for the 1,000 units of crude oil that you have just used and total up the revenues that you collect from the finished products, using the prices in Table 9.8.

Table 9.8

Crude-oil costs ($/unit)		Sales revenues ($/unit)	
Arabian	16.0	Liquid petroleum gases (LPG)	20
Brent	18.0	Motor oils	24
Gulf	14.0	Jet fuels	17
Venezuelan	9.0	Diesel oils	10
Trinidad	9.5	Fuel oils	6
East Texan	14.0		
West Texan	15.5		
Oklahoma	14.0		
Nigerian	12.0		
Libyan	17.0		

By subtracting total costs from total revenue you get a rough idea of the profit that your schedule would earn. It is an overestimate because in practice one also subtracts from your figure other refinery charges, notably materials (e.g. catalyst and lead additives), utilities (e.g. water and electricity charges), storage, repair, and labour costs and rates. But the cost and revenue of oil products completely dominate these other expenses.

Optional, more difficult exercise

Can you find a legitimate schedule that earns the refinery a profit if the following extra constraints must be met? As well as using less than or equal to 1,000 units of crude:

(i)   no more than 100 units of LPG must be produced;
(ii) input into the Polymerisation plant must be no greater than 100;
(iii) input into the Alkylation plant must be no greater than 100.

Further Analysis of Refinery Scheduling

If you have access to a computer package, this particular problem is amenable to an LP solution. However it will take quite a time to write in the data, as it involves 49 basic variables and 46 constraints. The 49 basic variables are the 10 crude inputs and the 39 arrowed pipelines. The 46 constraints are made up of 3 plant capacities, 1 demand limit, 8 blending constraints, 10 tank balances and 24 constraints for each yield coming out of a plant. (An example of a yield constraint would be 'propane ≤ 0.1 straight-run naphtha'.)

Having introduced what seems like quite a detailed problem it is now necessary to sound a word of warning. This model, with about 50 constraints and about 50 variables is still a gross approximation. At any normal-sized refinery or chemical plant there will be at least twenty major groups of finished products, at least twenty major processing plants and, between them, hundreds of pipelines. Also, we have brought in only a few simple constraints. In reality, there are an enormous number of other constraints, concerning a product's volatility, viscosity, octane rating, sulphur content, gravity and purity. Not all of these constraints can be expressed as linear equations for an LP. Nevertheless, LP serves its purpose as a global rough-cut planning technique.

On Using the Appropriate Scheduling Technique

We have covered quite a range of scheduling situations and techniques. Few of these techniques are universally applicable and many require management to invest resources in software, training or systems-reorganisation. This section reviews and consolidates the points which are relevant when deciding which scheduling techniques to adopt. It helps to do this by applying this checklist to the particular situation you are investigating.

Checklist

Demand characteristics:
- value
- turnover

- price variations
- quality variations
- derived demand
- customer's vulnerability to suppliers

Scheduling characteristics:

- length of order lead times
- manufacturing lead times
- distribution lead times
- material handling and storage problems
- product variety
- sequence of processes
- time horizons

Cost characteristics:

- cash-flow timings
- overheads
- special storage costs

Use of this Checklist

Just as the strength of a chain is the same as its weakest link, so the strength of a scheduling system is in its all-round coverage. If just one characteristic in the above lists is ignored, the scheduling system can collapse. For example, a firm making industrial furnaces needed small quantities of zirconium wire coming to only a few pence per furnace (the total value of these furnaces was £800 – £2,000). There was only one supplier of zirconium but he was reliable and always delivered promptly so that there was 'no need to hold much stock'. Then there was a fire at the supplier's factory. Everyone who needed zirconium bought every bit in Western Europe before the furnace manufacturer could get any. He had to run at 50 per cent capacity for two months.

In the above case the furnace manufacturer was plain unlucky. But often firms are careless in the characteristics they ignore. And sometimes a management method reinforces this carelessness. For example, there is a popular 'ABC analysis' which focuses rather inordinately on value and turnover characteristics. It groups together A items accounting for 70 per cent of turnover value and monitors them closely and frequently; it groups together B items accounting for 20 per cent of turnover value and has a less frequent review system for them; for the remaining C items, any cheap, crude method will do.

The zirconium example highlights the danger of using ABC analysis blindly. Use it only as a rough diagnostic starting point.

Summary and Overview of Operational Planning

Though planning problems come in all sizes and varieties, certain common themes emerge.

(1) The paramount importance of the information base All data used by planners are subject to similar problems of forecasting inaccuracy, imprecision or recording errors.

(2) Structuring operational-planning problems as cash flows over time Such a structure keeps close to a primary objective of most firms to earn the best string of profits possible. If problems are not structured in this way, and other criteria are employed, they need to be explicitly justified.

(3) Diagrammatic representation of operational plans An old Chinese proverb says 'a picture is worth a thousand words'. In the case of plans it is the *diagram* which makes understandable all the numbers, calculations and processes involved. These diagrams may be maps, networks, matrices or decision flow charts.

(4) Splitting problems Very occasionally, it has been possible to take a complex operating problem, feed all the data into one big model on a main-frame computer and wait for an all-singing, all-dancing package to churn out the answer. Personally, we would not recommend any such package where few people understand its internal mechanisms. An alternative approach is to find out how a complex problem can be split into smaller sub-problems and to develop easy-to-understand approaches for each of these.

(5) Difficulties in applying classical mathematical techniques Although mathematicians have given much attention to certain applications (TSP, LP), there is not much scope for classical optimisation (e.g. via calculus or simultaneous equations). This is because of the frequent appearance of step intervals and discontinuities (e.g. set-up costs, down-times, switching costs, discrete container sizes, non-continuous shift working). Alternative techniques (integer and dynamic programming) can handle only very small artificial problems even with modern computing power.

(6) Applying heuristics By this we mean:

    (i)   applying mixed rules of thumb to parts of a big problem so that a feasible schedule can be generated quickly;

    (ii)   quickly generating another and another and another schedule, using other rules of thumb to determine what changes to make.

Heuristics have always been the dominant technique employed in the foreman's office or by the majority of managers who have to handle a day-to-day series of crises. A few years ago there was a feeling that the computer revolution would lead to the replacement of heuristics by more scientific methods. In fact, the reverse has happened. Using spreadsheets or graphic modelling, more and more white-collar professionals are adopting the sort of heuristic techniques that we have been outlining in this chapter.

(7) Feedback and control Information coming into an organisation can be absorbed quickly or slowly. Likewise an organisation's response can be speedy or sluggish. An operational planner has to tailor his or her schedules to the 'nervousness' of the particular organisation. Hopefully it is better than this comment by a planner: 'My firm is like a rickety car. I push down the accelerator and nothing happens. I put on the brakes and nothing happens either.'

(8) Push-down, pop-up problems In medical terms this is attacking the (secondary) symptoms rather than the (primary) root cause of a disease. So a planner may resolve personal pressures whilst causing tremendous stresses in a supplier, customer or another department (refer to the Harry Britton case in Chapter 4 to see what the Accounts Department did to the transport scheduler). Or, to clear a backlog, high overtime hours might be regularly worked. This frequently leads to a fall in productivity during normal working hours. Or, if priority is given to the customer who shouts loudest, the word soon gets around and an increasing number of customers start to bully you. Or, if you get known as 'the planner who can always get us out of a crisis', people don't take the normal precautions to avoid such crises. Such are the tribulations of a very important but often under-appreciated member of the management team.

Further Reading

Standard Texts

Adam and Ebert (1986) Chapter 16.
Burbidge (1971) Chapters 13 and 21.
Chase and Aquilano (1981) Chapter 14.
Dilworth (1986) Chapters 7 and 8.
Evans *et al.* (1987) Chapters 13 – 16.
Hunter (1983) Chapter 10.
Krajewski and Ritzman (1987) Chapter 14.
Lewis (1981) Chapters 17 – 19.
Lockyer (1975) Chapters 10 – 12.

Lockyer (1986) Chapters 23−6.
McClain and Thomas (1980) Chapter 11.
Monks (1985) Chapter 10.
Stevenson (1986) Chapters 9 and 11.

Specialist Texts

Lockyer, K. (1966) *Practical Stock Control,* Pitman. This book keeps the needs of the practitioner very much in mind, even to the extent of having a book of worksheets to fill in.

Garvin, W.W. (1960) *Introduction to Linear Programming,* McGraw-Hill. Still the clearest and most authoritative work, written by a close associate of George Dantzig, the founder of linear programming. Modern writers on production scheduling are just rediscovering formulations explained by Dantzig and Garvin many years ago.

Case Studies

Constable (1976) Berger Paints Distribution (vehicle scheduling); Bridge Electric (A) (assembly-line balancing).

Meier (1982) Aerodyne (MPS); Maynard (MPS); Osburn (work scheduling); Othello (line balancing); Southern Hydraulic (ROQ/ROL).

Nicholson (1978) Medina (scheduling); Van Heugten (ROQ/ROL).

Schmenner (1986) Macpherson (MPS); Lamson (ROQ/ROL); Kumera (scheduling).

Chapter 10

PROJECT PLANNING

Introduction

Any project, whether it be installing a new computer in a building society or organising the London Marathon, requires planning. Connected with any such projects there will be several interested parties. For example, if we consider the construction of a building we have:

The client – 'I want this sort of building at this cost by this date.'

The architect – 'I will provide you with a design, structure and materials to be used.'

The quantity surveyor – 'I can procure the right amount of materials.'

The building inspector – 'Does this plan meet our safety, services and sightline regulations?'

The builder – 'How can I get this building up in view of the help (and hindrance) of the above professionals?'

Enter the *project planner* – 'How can I help the builder by devising a properly ordered schedule of jobs to be done?'

Depending on the size of the project and the managerial skill of the builder, different methods of planning and control are needed.

At the simplest level, this would involve a notebook or diary which the builder carries with him. As complexity increases, the building would need a week-by-week list of jobs for each worker, stating:

- the conditions necessary before the work can start;
- the resources necessary to do the job;
- how the job should be done;
- how often reports should be made, and to whom, on how the job is getting on.

For more complex cases still, a bar chart is often used which extends at least a month forward from the present date and shows when jobs should be started and when they are expected to be finished. In these complex cases each job, such as the erection of scaffolding, will involve a small team of workers.

For a simple building job like an extension, using two or three workers, an experienced builder will know the length of time taken by each stage of the job, such as digging the foundations and plastering. In his head he will develop a rough plan and target date for completion of the whole job. For more complex cases, like a block of flats, with many more workers and more individual jobs, it becomes too hard for the builder to work a plan out in his head. He needs to write it down, formally expressing what he previously did automatically.

It is likely that in his head he said, 'First of all, I've got to dig the foundations and make the holes to key the new bricks into the existing wall. That will take so many days. I'd better order the window frames now because the delivery time is about two weeks. I can get Joe to mix the concrete for the foundations while I'm sorting the windows out...', and so on. Mentally, the builder is drawing up a project plan. He is developing precedence relationships, working out which jobs must happen before which other jobs and which jobs can go on simultaneously if his resources, the number of workers, allow this. He does this to work out how long the whole job will take so that he can give the customer a completion date. Then he has to make sure he sticks to the plan. If he falls behind, he'll need to shuffle his resources around or use extra resources, employing extra workers, to get back on target, unless he can negotiate a later completion date with the customer.

For any project we need to use a similar approach. Even activities which we would not recognise as 'projects' can benefit from project-planning techniques, e.g. co-ordinating all the activities associated with an aircraft 'turnaround' at an airport. This has many characteristics of a project. It is important to minimise turnaround time, since non-flying hours bring in no revenue. Extra resources in terms of workers and machinery can be allocated to speed up the work, but at a cost. Even with extra resources it would be hard to see how some activities, such as refuelling, could be speeded up. There is therefore only a certain degree of flexibility in reaching an agreed target time. This agreed time must be adhered to, and broken down into a bar chart so that every worker involved knows exactly what is to be done when. This bar chart showing personnel involved and the timing of their tasks is shown in Figure 10.1. Failure to meet the agreed time means that planes miss take-off slots, leading to delays. This has a knock-on effect at destination airports, costing money and causing frustration to passengers, airline and airport staff alike.

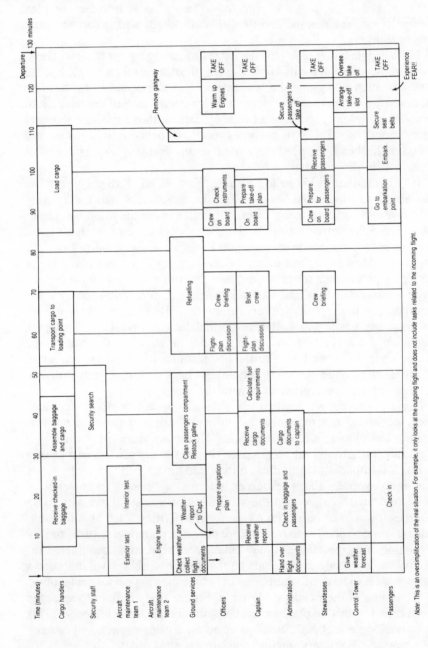

Figure 10.1 Aircraft turnaround

Note: This is an oversimplification of the real situation. For example, it only looks at the outgoing flight and does not include tasks related to the incoming flight.

Precedence Networks

Consider bringing a new high-technology product to the market. There would be a set of jobs which would have to be carried out. In the introduction we recognised that in a project certain jobs cannot start until other jobs have finished, but other jobs can go on quite independently and feed into the overall plan at a later stage.

To give the flavour of what an extract from a network for the design of a jet aircraft might look like, look at Figure 10.2.

The activity on the right-hand side may seem trivial compared with the others, but aircraft have crashed through the faulty design of a door lock. Therefore a final network must be ready to include microscopic detail. But suppose you start drawing a network by amassing an enormous number of small activities? The odds are that you will end up with a tangle of precedences. In all probability vital precedences will be missed out — the very eventuality you wish to avoid. It is better to start off by constructing a complete network consisting of a few general activities, then breaking it down and expanding it.

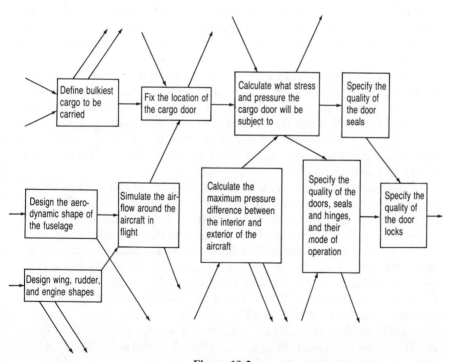

Figure 10.2

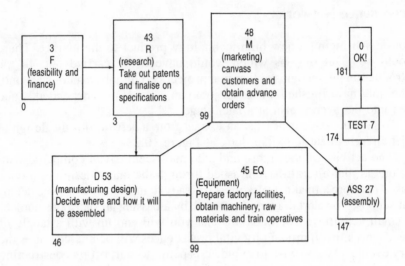

Figure 10.3

Refer to Figure 10.3. Suppose we need to know how long the whole project will take. The numbers in the boxes show the estimated duration time for each stage of the project in months. Knowing how each job fits in with the others and using the arrows, we can calculate how long the whole project will take.

Starting on the left-hand side we will set the first job F to start at zero time. Therefore we put 0 under the F box on the left-hand side. If F takes 3 months, then the earliest R can start is after those 3 months have elapsed. You might think that job R therefore starts at the beginning of month 4, which is true. However, as we started at time zero, logically we need to put a 3 on the left-hand side under box R to indicate the *earliest start time* (EST) of job R.

Continuing with this, we find the earliest job D can start is 46 and so on. We have two arrows coming out of D, leading to M and EQ. This means neither M nor EQ can start until D has finished but they are independent of each other and can be carried out simultaneously.

Both can therefore start at 46 + 53 = 99, but the next job, ASS, cannot start until both M and EQ have finished. The earliest M can finish is 99 + 48 = 147 and the earliest EQ can finish is 99 + 45 = 144, so that although job EQ allows ASS to start at 144, job M holds it up until 147. Therefore the EST of ASS is 147.

TEST can then start at 147 + 27 = 174 and the project could finish at 181. (Convention requires us to put a finish box into our network, which does not take any time up.)

What we have done so far is known as a *forward pass*. We have calculated the earliest start times of each activity in the network and found the minimum time in which the project can be completed, within the existing resource constraints. In fact the whole project will take less time than this because there is almost bound to be some overlap between these general activities. Each of these activities can be broken down into small activities and new precedences drawn up which are less restrictive than the old ones. Consider an extension to the network in Figure 10.3. It is likely that a pilot or Mark I model will have to be made to sort out major problems. The customers will take delivery of the Mark II model, which should then have had all the problems encountered in the Mark I model ironed out. To incorporate this, our network needs to be extended as shown in Figure 10.4.

You will see that work from Mark I is being fed into Mark II as the project progresses. The key shows the further splits made to activities. You will also see that more numbers have appeared on the network. For the moment, just look at the durations (in the boxes) and the ESTs under the left-hand side of each box.

Exercise

1. Do a forward pass on this new network to check out EST figures.
2. Do you feel the activities have been given the correct precedence relationships? If not, amend the network and recalculate the earliest time in which the job can be completed.

Critical Path

You should have found that some jobs are completed well before a following job can begin because another job holds the project up. D_1 holds up D_2 although R_2 has finished. It is important to identify these jobs which hold up the network. They are known as *critical* jobs. If one of these jobs gets behind schedule, then the whole project falls behind. To work out which these jobs are, we need to start at the end of the network and work backwards, finding out the latest time each job can finish whilst allowing the whole project to be completed by the calculated time. This is what the number on the right-hand side under each box represents — the *latest finish time* (LFT) of each activity.

Using Figure 10.4, we can see that OK finishes at 146 and takes 0 time, thus the latest $TEST_2$ can finish is 146. If $TEST_2$ can finish at 146,

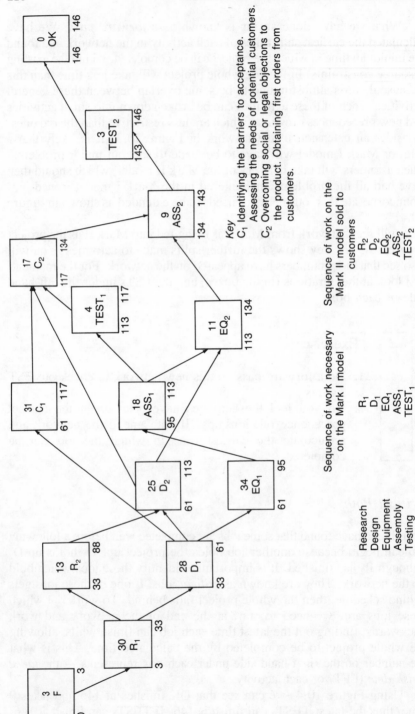

Figure 10.4 Extended network

Research
Design
Equipment
Assembly
Testing

Sequence of work necessary
on the Mark I model

R_1
D_1
EQ_1
ASS_1
$TEST_1$

Sequence of work on the
Mark II model sold to
customers

R_2
D_2
EQ_2
ASS_2
$TEST_2$

Key
C_1 Identifying the barriers to acceptance.
Assessing the needs of potential customers.
C_2 Overcoming social or legal objections to
the product. Obtaining first orders from
customers.

then the latest ASS_2 can finish is 143, because $TEST_2$ takes three months. We can work backwards through C_2's LFT $= 143 - 9 = 134$, EQ_2's LFT $= 143 - 9 = 134$, and $TEST_1$'s LFT $= 134 - 17 = 117$.

What happens when we get to ASS_1? The LFT of $EQ_2 = 134$ and it takes eleven months. Therefore if ASS_1 just needed to meet the requirements of EQ_2 then it could finish at 123 and the whole project would still be on time. However, the LFT of $TEST_1 = 117$ and it takes four months. Therefore to get $TEST_1$ started to meet the project deadline, the latest ASS_1 can finish is $117 - 4 = 113$. Keep working backwards like this and see if you can confirm our LFT figures.

We are now in a position to work out which activities are *critical* i.e. those in which (LFT $-$ EST) $=$ duration of the activity. Check through Figure 10.4 and find out which jobs are critical. You'll find there are 10 critical jobs and all are connected on a pathway leading from the start of the project to the finish. This pathway is known as the *critical path*. Figure 10.5 shows the critical path marked in bold.

Floats

Jobs not on the critical path have some 'slack'. In others words, the duration of the jobs was less than the time allowed between the LFT and the EST. So can they be done any time during this period? The answer is not totally straightforward. We have to say, sometimes yes and sometimes no.

This is best explained by a simpler example. You can go back later and sort out the floats associated with the jobs in Figure 10.5. Let us take a network with just six jobs shown in Figure 10.6. We have calculated the ESTs, the LFTs, the project duration in hours and the critical path.

The following section explains the meaning of the number shown in brackets under the activities B and C. Jobs B, C and D all have some slack, but how much?

Let us look at Job C. The earliest time C *could* start is 4, but it couldn't start at time 4, unless B had finished by then. To keep the project on target, B does not have to finish until time 18, so clearly *both* B and C cannot use up all the slack they seem to have from our EST and LFT calculations. B's total float is (LFT $-$ EST $-$ duration) $= (18 - 2 - 2) = 14$ but that is not independent of the float that C apparently has of $(45 - 4 - 2) = 39$. The total float of B and C together is only (LFT of C $-$ EST of B $-$ duration of C $-$ duration of B) $= (45 - 2 - 2 - 2) = 39$. Fourteen of C's float is shared with B. Therefore we can say that B and C have a *shared float* of 14.

Even if B takes all of this shared float, C will not become critical. If the job started at 18, the latest time B could finish, C takes only 2 hours and you've got until time 45 to do the job, therefore C still has 25 hours

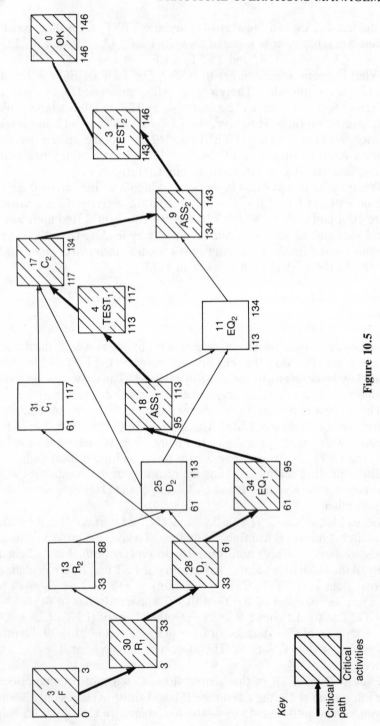

Figure 10.5

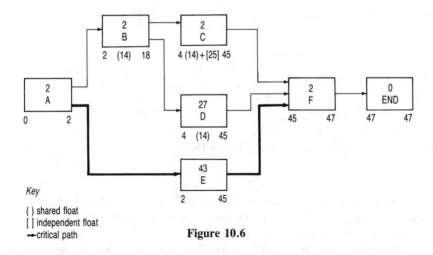

Key
( ) shared float
[ ] independent float
→critical path

Figure 10.6

slack. This slack is known as an *independent float* because it cannot be shared with any other job.

These floats are fundamental concepts in critical-path analysis and you will find they crop up in most examples when you have networks of any size. We have represented them by further numbers under the activity boxes. Shared floats are shown in round brackets and independent floats in square brackets. The floats for B and C have been shown in Figure 10.6. Why is there only a shared float for D?

Dummy Activities

Our networks, so far, have been fairly easy to follow. Sometimes in big projects we find arrows crisscrossing over each other to such an extent that the network becomes unintelligible. A way round this is to introduce *dummy* activities. Suppose we had eight jobs and they were connected as shown in Figure 10.7.

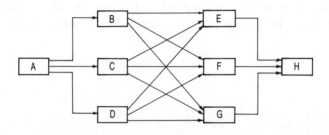

Figure 10.7

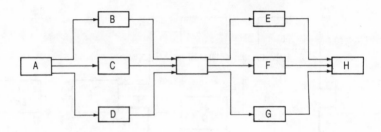

Figure 10.8

Even in this simple case, the situation becomes confused. A dummy activity, which has a duration of 0 time, can be inserted between activities BCD and EFG as shown in Figure 10.8.

This shows that B C and D must all be completed before the dummy can start and E F and G cannot start until it has finished. As you can see it simply tidies up the network without changing the logic.

Network Design

Often we cannot design the whole project network in one stage. We often need to look at blocks of jobs and how the jobs within those blocks are linked before seeing how the whole network fits together. This is illustrated by another simple example: changing a car wheel following a puncture (see Table 10.1).

To draw up the project network we need to unravel the precedence relationships of the blocks of jobs. The slash-symbol means that all activities to the left of the symbol must be done before any activity on the right of the symbol can begin. For example, D and H must be completed before I or M can start. E must be completed before F, L or D can start.

Taking all these relatiohships from the blocks into account, let us start building up the total network. We know B must precede all other activities, so we can put B on the left-hand side. We know all other activities must precede N, so that goes on the right-hand side. C and F must precede G

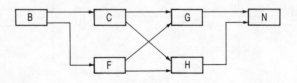

Figure 10.9

Table 10.1

List of activities

Duration (minutes)	Code	Description
2	B	Locate and check all tools needed (mallet, jack, screwdriver, 2 brace-spanners, extension rod)
4	C	Find and place chockstones to stop car rolling (using a mallet)
4	D	Remove spare wheel (using a brace-spanner)
1	E	Remove hubcap (using screwdriver)
2	F	Lightly loosen the wheelnuts of the flat tyre (brace-spanner and extension rod for leverage)
3	G	Jack up car (brace-spanner and jack)
2	H	Remove wheelnuts and wheel
2	I	Put on spare wheel and lightly fix wheelnuts
3	J	Lower and remove jack (brace-spanner and jack)
2	K	Tighten wheel nuts (brace-spanner) and replace hubcap (mallet)
2	L	Remove chockstones (screwdriver)
4	M	Stow away wheel with defective tyre (brace-spanner)
1	N	Replace tools

Precedence relationships

B/All other activities
All other activities/N
CF/GH
DH/IM
E/FLD
F/GK
G/HJD
I/JK
HJ/L
M/J

and H, so we must add those between B and N. We connect these boxes up by arrows to show the precedence relationships and arrive at Figure 10.9.

Continuing like this, we can connect up further boxes as shown in Figure 10.10. And having now dealt with five of the precedence blocks, if we add in the remaining five we arrive at Figure 10.11.

You can see that we have quite a muddle. Even so, we cheated and did not join B or N up to every job otherwise the network would have been completely unintelligible. We waited until we had joined all the other boxes together and then joined B and N only to those with which it was necessary, i.e. all activities from B are reached through C or E and all activities reaching N are channelled through K or L.

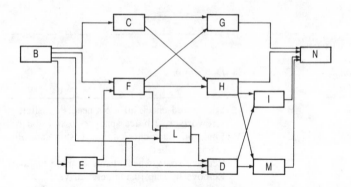

Figure 10.10

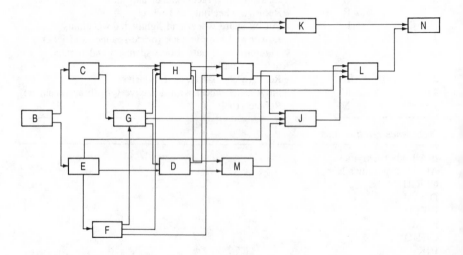

Figure 10.11

Redundant arrows   We can take this further and look at all the other arrows in Figure 10.11. We certainly have unnecessary, *redundant*, arrows included here, which need to be eliminated for the sake of clarity. The arrow between E and D is redundant, since E is already preceding D via F and G. Similarly the arrow between F and H can be eliminated and so on. You should try this for yourself.

You can introduce a dummy between HD and IM and make the picture even clearer. Making this amendment and using the durations given in Table 10.1 we have drawn up Figure 10.12. We have calculated the time the whole job will take and have shown the critical path and the floats associated with the various activities.

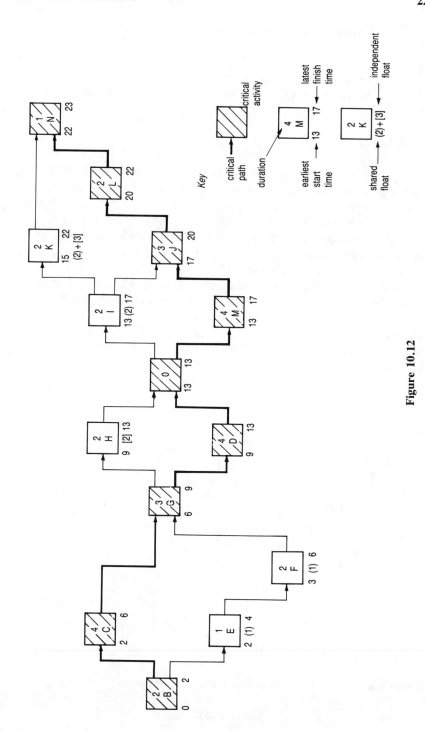

Figure 10.12

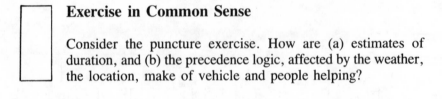

Exercise in Common Sense

Consider the puncture exercise. How are (a) estimates of duration, and (b) the precedence logic, affected by the weather, the location, make of vehicle and people helping?

Bar Charts

Our representation of a project has so far been in network form. Whilst this may be useful for the planner, it is not a good way to communicate what work needs to be done when, and by whom, to the workforce. A much better method of communication is a bar chart, which shows, for each day or week or month depending on the duration of each job, what job each worker, or group of workers, is supposed to be doing. This can be illustrated using changing the car wheel as an example.

Working from the network diagram Figure 10.12, we can construct the bar chart shown in Figure 10.13. Critical activities have been shaded.

We can then allocate jobs to the occupants of the afflicted car. Suppose there were two people – let's call them X and Y – in the car and all job times were calculated on the basis of only one worker doing each job. Then we can show on another bar chart what X and Y could be doing

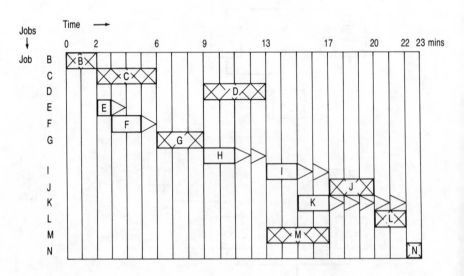

Total float is shown on non-critical jobs by the symbol > (each > represents 1 minute).

Figure 10.13

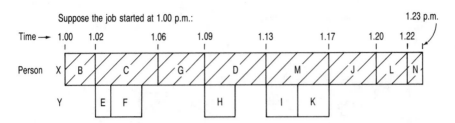

The float on non-critical activities has not been shown here. The blocks represent the duration times in Figure 10.12.

Figure 10.14   Resource allocation

throughout the process. This is shown in Figure 10.14. Critical activities have again been shaded.

As you can see Y is getting a fairly easy time compared with X. In this particular situation it is probably not too important that Y is wasting 14 minutes out of a total of 23 minutes.

In a project where a budget was involved this would be unacceptable. Maybe the jobs X did on his own could be done faster if Y gave a hand, in which case the network would need to be recalculated, allowing for the changes in duration times. Such resource reallocation is essential in big projects to keep costs down and to reduce overall job times by eliminating bottlenecks.

Exercise in Critical-path Analysis and Resource Allocation

Figure 10.15 represents a simplified project plan for building a new university. The number in each box is the duration in months of the activity in question. Suppose that you are the manager responsible for completing the project.

Determine the total project time and find the critical path.

The planned completion date is synchronised with the start of an academic year so it is vital that it is met. The following difficulties arise:

1. The architect requests an extra month to prepare the design. What is your reaction?
2. You have started the Library on schedule. Your assistant reports that because of unanticipated ground conditions the block will take fourteen months to construct instead of eleven. How concerned are you?

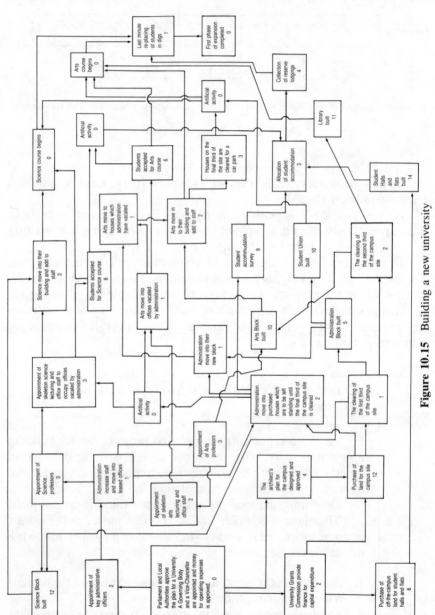

Figure 10.15 Building a new university

3. It has taken four months to allocate student accommodation. The vice-chancellor asks you if the time could be made up by reducing the time allocated to collecting reserve lodgings. What do you say?

4. Administration proposes to take three months instead of two to move into the purchased houses. The chief administrator (who once read an article on project planning in *Administration Today*) says he is aware that this task is critical but he will make up for it by allocating extra staff to the accommodation survey, thereby reducing its duration from nine to eight months. What is your reply?

5. It transpires that the Administration Block takes seven months to build. Explain to your assistant what the implications of this are for the construction of the Student Union.

6. The roofing-tile supplier goes bankrupt with the consequence that the Arts Block is delayed by a month. Report to the governing body on the various courses of action which would compensate for this event.

7. You sanctioned a six-month extension to the time allocated to the Arts Faculty for the appointment of skeleton staff. Subsequently the Science Faculty wants a similar extension. Comment.

8. Could you redesign the network so that there is a less confusing layout?

Implementation

So far we have dealt with the planning side of the project. When a project has been planned, that is only the beginning. Many a seemingly perfect plan has faltered in the implementation stage.

Two British companies joined forces in 1982 to take on a prestigious £25 million contract to build a new zoo in Saudi Arabia. Right at the start the contractors hit their first problem, the animals. The contract involved demolishing the old zoo before starting work on the new one. However when the contractors arrived to start work, they found that not only were the buildings and cages still there but so were the zoo staff and the animals. Obviously there were delays while these hindrances were disposed of.

Water was the next problem. Initially one supply was required in the contract from an underground reservoir. This was changed to two supplies, one for drinking and one for irrigation. Because of the risk of animals drinking the impure irrigation water, the client asked for a water-purification plant to be installed. Fifteen months after the start of the project, the client had another change of heart and decided that maybe one supply was best after all.

Changes were then requested to the electricity supply, and so it went on. The problems were compounded by the local company which was supervising the project. It was not in a position to give definite yes or no answers to questions. Such questions had to be referred 'higher up', causing more delays. The project was planned to take two years. Even with a five-month extension and a £2.5 million increase in costs it was still impossible to meet the deadline. The company decided to cut its losses and pull out, having learnt some valuable lessons.

The chief executive of a large, experienced contracting firm believes that there are two basic secrets to successful project implementation:

(i)   finding the right partners;
(ii)   not being so hungry for work that you go in, full of enthusiasm, to secure a project at all costs.

Even getting this right, companies have found to their cost that you need to 'understand the local mentality' and develop skills in working with local contractors and consultants.

Many contractors do get it right. For example Esso's £400 million ethylene plant at Mossmorran in Fife, Scotland was completed five months ahead of schedule and 5 per cent below budget. The contractors put their success down to achieving 20 per cent better productivity than budgeted and the fact that industrial disputes took up only 1.2 per cent of the total manhours. This is one-third of the level generally experienced on such projects. Industrial relations problems were at the forefront of the contractor's mind before starting on the project, and a site industrial relations manager was appointed well before any earth was moved. Although both unions and management badly needed success after the construction fiascos of the 1970s, particularly involving nuclear power stations, that success had to be planned for. Typical of the planning was the care taken during the rundown period. Workers see redundancy looming and go-slows become familiar. A job information service was set up on site, which placed some 60 per cent of workers in new jobs.

Computer Packages

Calculations by hand can be tedious. Many computer packages are now available which can produce project plans faster than by hand and do reallocation calculations much faster.

These range from simple packages which run on micros to more complex packages running on mainframes. Such advances have been made recently that even the micro packages can deal with complex networks effectively. Calendars are built into many programs. So weekends and holidays are automatically accounted for in project duration time calculations. Sophisticated printers allow bar charts to be produced, colour-coded, straight off the computer for easy understanding by groups of workers who just look for their assigned colour. Sophisticated packages are now beginning to change the emphasis of the planning by looking at the people concerned rather than the tasks to be done. This is not important if we are trying to build a house. Any competent bricklayer will do and if one is ill or leaves the project will not be affected. However, the same cannot be said of skilled professional personnel. A replacement cannot just pick up the threads and carry on from where another person left off. If this were possible, the temporary employment agencies would long since have been in this business.

CASE STUDY: PROBLEMS IN INTRODUCING A NEW COMPUTER SYSTEM

A retailing organisation wanted to upgrade its computer system. Around the United Kingdom the company had almost 100 branches. No computer link existed between these branches and Head Office. All data were sent from the branches to Head Office in printed form through the post. The company required:

(i)   a branch system primarily to deal with inventory management, sales-order processing, purchase-order processing and back orders, including a facility to send information between Head Office and the branches down a telephone line;

(ii) A new sales ledger system.

Head Office was also about to be moved to a new building, so it was decided to undertake both projects, the installation of the computer system and the move, simultaneously.

Several systems were investigated. Alternative hardware and software was considered. One system seemed to satisfy all requirements with minimal modification, except in one respect. Branch managers would have to send tapes to Head Office. The information could not be transmitted down the telephone lines. This option was therefore rejected.

During this search a senior manager happened to be in America. Whilst there, he was shown a software package in operation which seemed to satisfy all his needs. The decision was made to purchase the package and the project was under-way. Time estimates were made for various tasks and a project plan was drawn up, using a computer package. This incorporated the move to new premises and the introduction of a new computer system. The plan is shown in Figure 10.16.

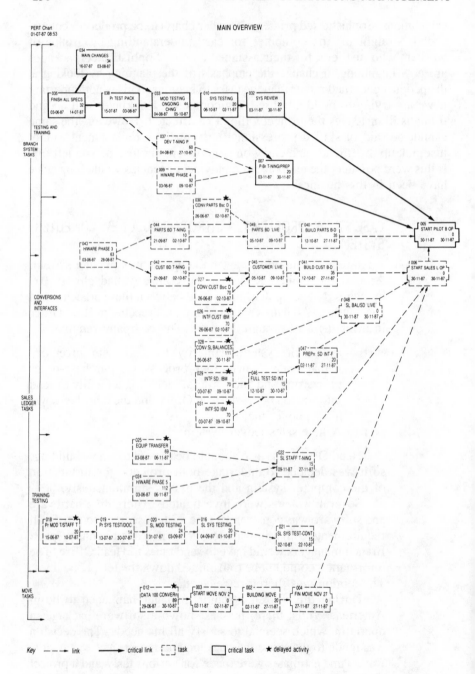

Figure 10.16 Original plan

All tasks have been abbreviated to fit into the boxes. Some will be meaningful to you and some will not. (But they give you a flavour of large projects.)

The plan was built up from three major separate groups of tasks:

(i)   the move to new premises
(ii) the sales ledger system
(iii) the branch system

NB You will notice that there is not one single starting point for the network. Jobs 009, 024, 035 and 043 all have an earliest start time of 3.6.1987. This is therefore the start date of the project. However jobs 012, 018, 025, 026, 027, 028, 029, 030 and 031 have been *allocated* ESTs later than 3.6.1987, although none of these jobs requires the completion of any other job before it can begin. These jobs have been marked with an asterisk and labelled 'delayed' activities in Figure 10.16.

Such jobs have been allocated these later dates using common sense. It did not seem sensible to start on conversion tasks until the project was well under way. Hence jobs 029 and 031, for example, were allocated ESTs of 3.7.1987, one month into the project, although in principle they could have started on 3.6.87. This multiple-start idea is common in large projects.

Work started on the project. The systems team prepared the specifications for the branch software package (Task 035) falling one week behind schedule, then sent them to the American software house for the necessary modifications to the package to be made (Task 034). Here further problems started. The work started one week late because of the late specifications. The modifications were extensive and the software house had problems tailoring the package. The project fell four weeks behind schedule. Communications flew back and forth over the Atlantic between the UK and USA. This meant that the project could not be completed by the scheduled date since these tasks were on the critical path.

It was clear that, although the first revised modules had been received (Task 034), there were many other modifications necessary to make the package work successfully for the company. Extra time had to be allowed for this work. Taking into account other problems encountered, particularly on interfacing, the project schedule was extensively revised on 18 September 1987 with a new completion date, some four months later than the original planned date. The revised plan is shown as a bar (Gantt) chart in Figure 10.17.

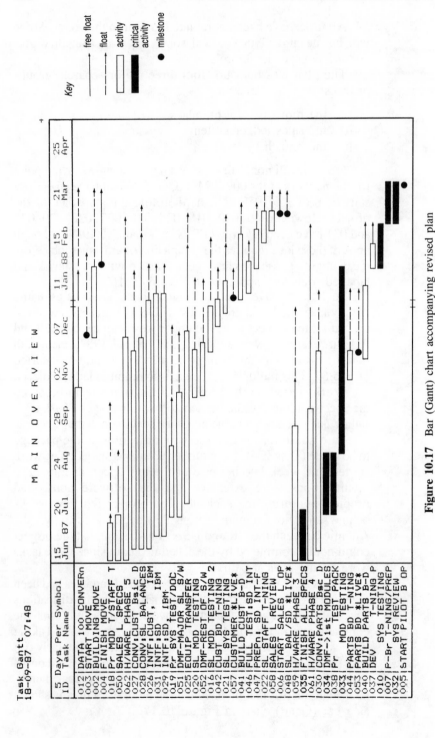

Figure 10.17 Bar (Gantt) chart accompanying revised plan

You will see that total floats and free floats have been shown on the bar (Gantt) chart. These are to tell you how much you can overrun certain tasks and still keep the total project on schedule. Also included are 'milestones'. These are exactly what they say — milestones (or 'deadlines') in the project, e.g.:

004 Finish move
057 Go live with conversion of customer data on to new sales ledger system

Comment   At the time of writing the project is still underway. The problems encountered are typical of those in any project. When several sub-projects need to be co-ordinated, delay in any one causes delays in completion of the overall project. Overoptimism is a frequent problem in computer systems installations and buying software from a distant source is generally unadvisable unless you are 100 per cent sure it will work on the planned hardware without modification and do exactly what you want it to — a situation almost unheard-of in computer systems work.

Further Reading

Standard Texts

Lockyer (1986) Chapter 7.
Schmenner (1987) Chapter 4, Appendix C.

Specialist Texts

Mulvaney,J.E. (1975) *ABC Analysis Bar Charting*, Mantec. The author who first emphasised that practitioners prefer precedence networks.
Lockyer,K. (1984) *Critical Path Analysis*, 4th edn, Pitman. Thoroughly revamped to incorporate the precedence network approach.
The user's guide to software packages are also a good source of information for precedence-network methods.

Case Studies

Meier (1982) Petersen.

———————————— Chapter 11 ————————————

OPERATIONS MANAGEMENT IN THE CONTEXT OF GENERAL MANAGEMENT

Throughout this book we have related the activities and problems of operations managers:

- upwards, to the objectives of the organisation as a whole;
- sideways, to other functional areas.

Let us gather together the points we have made and focus on these upwards and sideways relationships.

In Chapter 1, *Scope,* managers of retailing, transport, service and manufacturing activities described their jobs. We saw how in the case of the public-sector bus operator the enforced change from running a public service to a commercial enterprise affected the organisation's objectives. This worked its way down to a tightening up of day-to-day operations. Similarly the corporate policy of the department store group to encourage inter-branch competition had a direct effect on the working rosters of staff to ensure merchandise reached the selling floor faster. Clearly the situation and policies of the organisation have a direct impact on operations.

In Chapter 2, *The Product,* the sideways relationships between the operations, marketing and finance functions were clearly seen in the development and assessment of a new product. Marketing must answer the question, 'Is there a market?' Finance must decide, 'Does it make financial sense?' Operations must decide, 'Can we provide it?' But this in itself is not enough: the process, as we saw, is cyclical. The three functions must work to an overall integrated plan with specific time horizons.

As well as these sideways interactions, we have upward considerations. The product must fit in with corporate objectives. For example in a food company the marketing function may find there is a market for a new extra-sticky toffee, the operations function may have the capability to produce it and the finance function may approve the budget for it. But, if the company has positioned itself in the 'health-food business', the new product would not be in harmony with its corporate philosophy and the company would be unlikely to go ahead.

In Chapter 3, *Machines,* we saw the need for financial analysis when making machine purchase decisions. Again, sideways interaction is necessary to reach the right decision.

In Chapter 4, *People,* we explained how the various levels of an organisation have different objectives and how, if all these objectives are in accord, the organisation is more effective. We saw how a seemingly straightforward operational problem, 'What can we do about Harry Britton?', requires a hierarchy of objectives, strategies, plans and procedures in its solution, not restricted to the operations function but having impact higher up the organisation.

In Chapter 5, *Materials,* we considered the difference between strategic, tactical and routine decisions in purchasing. Strategic decisions above the operations manager determine such things as backward integration (the buying up of suppliers) and forward integration (the buying up of outlets). This is the province of the general manager but has a major impact on the operations function.

In Chapter 6, *Quality,* we put over the message that quality assurance is not restricted to the operations function. Quality assurance spans every aspect of the business, sideways and upwards. The British Standards Institute stress this by their desire to see the managing director of an organisation given the title of Quality Assurance Manager, showing a company-wide commitment to quality.

In Chapter 7, *Systems,* in the Push and Pull experiments, we saw how workforce motivation and innovation could be influenced by the design of the operational system. In the Pull experiment, the system encouraged the fastest team of workers to help other teams in the system. This led to shop-floor workers thinking of innovative ways to speed up certain jobs. The more communal, cohesive practices of the workforce set the tone for the whole organisation.

In Chapter 8, *Forecasting,* we examined the impact on operations of wider influences beyond the organisation. The business environment, customers, suppliers and competitors all have effects which filter down to the operations function.

In Chapter 9, *Operational Planning*, we took the primary objective of planning — 'to attain the best long-run stream of profits' — and worked down from this corporate requirement to short-term operational schedules. We saw that operational scheduling cannot be viewed in isolation. Local priority rules, even if they minimise wasted time on a particular machine, may have devastating effects on the business if a key customer is kept waiting for a small but vital order.

The very essence of Chapter 10, *Project Planning*, is the integration of activities, at all levels and across all functions. But however intricate the sideways planning it must be able to cope with sudden changes in direction imposed from the top. The construction project to build a new zoo in the Middle East was a clear example of this.

The above recap re-emphasises that operations managers do not operate in a vacuum. Operations must tie in with the organisation as a whole: sideways, with the other functional areas of the organisation, and upwards, with the organisation's situation and objectives.

As we have been using terms such as strategies and objectives let us clearly define what we mean by them. Let us take a more formal look at an organisation and the hierarchy of activities which exists. Starting at the bottom, we have:

Procedures   These are clerical, semi-automatic operations which can be followed from a rule book. They are usually carried out by people at the bottom of the organisation. (E.g. ordering, invoicing, measuring, inspecting, recording, assembling, packing, cleaning, handling.)

Tactics   These are decisions delegated to the discretion of the frontline manager. (E.g. overtime arrangements, forward buying, priority scheduling, securing price discounts.)

Functional Strategies   Here we are moving still further up the organisation. These strategies are longer-term decisions affecting resource allocation within one function of the business. (E.g. marketing strategies (leader, niche, penetration, segmentation), subcontracting levels, make-or-buy policies.

Corporate Strategies   Further up the organisation still, we reach the strategies which affect the total business — the domain of the chief executive. (E.g. asset stripping, turnarounds, balancing portfolios, vertical integration, equity-based expansion.)

Corporate Objectives   These are significant long-term objectives for the organisation mutually agreed by the board and its major shareholders. (E.g. profit maximisation, minimisation of tax payments, maximisation of consumer goodwill, community approval or political influence.)

Stakeholder Activities   Higher still we find diplomacy and power struggles between those who have an influence on the organisation. These may be major shareholders, powerful unions or powerful consumer consortia. (E.g. takeover battles, legal battles on ownership and control, major showdowns and strikes, consumer boycotts.)

Ethos: Above all these levels are environmental influences in the widest sense. E.g. national culture, wealth, type of political system (communist, democratic, etc.), or level of strife (wars, civil disorder, etc.). It has been suggested that the Japanese economic success arose because they were on the losing side in the second world war, which led to a desire to 'show the world'. Coupled with their history of co-operative activity and conformity they did so successfully — many companies who have effectively been put out of business by Japanese competitors might argue *too successfully.*

So we have a hierarchy of terms from *procedures* to *ethos*. This hierarchy shows how operations fit in with the organisation as a whole. It has to be a generalisation. Large organisations can afford to have a management hierarchy to match the decision hierarchy. In small companies, however, with just one owner/general manager, a foreman and some operatives the boundaries can become less clear. The general manager will be making decisions at all levels, except maybe the procedural level. Such a system can be very effective. But as the business expands, the general manager may be in danger of 'not seeing the wood for the trees', spending too long on tactics and neglecting his corporate strategy. So even at small-company level the hierarchical approach can be a useful balancing mechanism.

Suppose we ask ourselves 'What comes first: decisions at the top of the tree or decisions at the bottom?' Arguments have been put forward for a rigid top-down approach such that:

> *Stakeholder Activities*
> determine
> *Corporate Objectives*
> determine
> *Functional Strategies*
> determine
> *Tactics*
> determine
> *Procedures*

In the recent past, this approach has led large organisations to set up corporate planning departments. Such departments were supposed to act as the 'Brain of the Firm', decisions being passed down as in the list above.

This style has now become less fashionable as the importance of interaction between all levels of an organisation has been recognised. It is better for the whole organisation to operate as one entity. For example, a tactic must be in harmony with other tactics in other functional areas, with procedures below it and with strategies above it. Likewise every strategy, objective, etc. must have a harmonic position in the whole organisation. This approach we feel is the key to success. Just grafting on one or two 'successful' techniques from other companies or countries will not necessarily work.

Let us take a few examples from operations management to illustrate the danger of piecemeal grafting.

Many Western companies have attempted to adopt Japanese techniques, for example:

Quality Circles (a *functional strategy*)
JIT Schedules (a *tactic*)
Kanbans (a *procedure*)

Quality Circles are unlikely to work unless the firm is offering the harmonic *corporate strategy* of long-term employment (very rarely the case in Western business).

As we noted in Chapter 9, JIT schedules will create disharmony if combined with the *functional strategy* of piece-rate schemes.

And (as we have implied in Chapter 7's Push−Pull experiments) Kanban cards are an integral part of commitment to quality (a *strategy*) and helping co-workers (part of a general *ethos*).

To repeat, whenever any new management system is installed, it must be in accord with all related procedural, tactical and strategic activities. It is for this reason that companies accepting this argument have concentrated on improving their corporate culture, as defined and discussed in Chapter 4.

To conclude the book we present a case study of a company with several unconventional policies which are nevertheless in harmony with each other. The company is successful and profitable.

CASE STUDY: SWITCH MANUFACTURER

This company has been manufacturing small electromechanical switches for 40 years. Its policies are described below:

(1) 'Never have a bank overdraft' What have been the implications of this? Customers have to pay invoices within seven days. They are encouraged to do this by the incentive of a discount. If they do not pay, it is not a matter of 'That's

OK, but you will pay the full price within thirty days', but 'Sorry, we have to stop supplying you.'

A casual observer might think that such a strict policy on customer payments would be commercial suicide. So it would be for a weak firm. But in this case the policy has *forced* the company to become more proficient in these ways:

- The product had to be sufficiently attractive to the customer for him to put up with this treatment, which meant offering unbeatable quality, reliability and technical service, and meeting promised delivery dates or whatever benefits were critical to the customer. This inevitably affected the operating side of the business.

- The company developed a relationship of absolute trust with the customer. Ironically, payment within seven days from customers with computerised purchase-order systems means the customer has no opportunity to check that the goods have actually arrived before paying. The invoice often has to be paid on sight in good faith.

What about the other side of the coin? How quickly does the company pay its suppliers? Local traders are paid within seven days, because the company wants to maintain a good local image and get good, quick service, so that the whole operation is not halted by a leaky roof or a plumbing problem. Other suppliers get paid on normal commercial terms. If they demand payment within 7 or 28 days, then the company respects that and pays up. But it takes full advantage of the time lag, as do most companies.

(2) 'Don't follow the crowd' The company makes small switches which are mounted inside electrical appliances. The company has purposefully designed the switches so that their mountings in the electrical appliances have to be different from the mountings needed for their competitors' switches. This, the company believes, will protect them from a price-cutting war since straight substitution is not possible. This has had a profound effect on design and selling, and filters through to the operations side. Selling is not done by the typical 'samples in a suitcase' approach. Instead, client contact starts far earlier, the company's engineers getting together with the appliance producers and designing the company's switches into the product. This 'exclusive' approach is acceptable to customers only because

the company can guarantee a reliable supply of switches. Usually reliance on one supplier is a situation many companies will not tolerate. The customers have to be totally convinced that there will be no strikes to interrupt the supply, so good labour relations, and hence attractive working terms and conditions, are essential (and so the chain of good practices gets extended).

(3) 'Keep manufacturing units small'   The company believes that there is an optimum size of production unit. When the number of employees on one production site reaches 150, the company looks for another site to develop. It believes the production manager loses personal contact with staff when sites get too big. Therefore, in terms of operations-management style, 'managing by walking around' is strictly the order of the day. An extension of this policy is to build new factories where government support is available, in far-flung corners of the UK. This has enormous implications for the operation, the major one being transportation. All material and finished products have to be transported over considerable distances. So it is impossible to have a close-knit Just-In-Time scheduling system. It does not matter to this company that it is not applying JIT because in its case the material content of the product is a relatively small percentage of the product cost.

(4) 'Don't locate units on industrial estates − locate units in the centre of small towns'   The sites chosen are never on industrial estates but preferably in small towns. This grew out of the use of female operatives. The management thinks a central location in a town is more attractive to its predominantly female labour force who find the environment more pleasant, and more convenient for lunchtime and early evening shopping. Thus the labour force is generally more contented. But it also means that the operation must be kept 'clean'. This is clearly not a policy that could be adopted by chemical companies, with the inherent risks to the population, or by those with effluent problems either liquid or gaseous.

Moral on this Case Study

Using just one example we can see that policy decisions have far-reaching effects on the operations side of the business, and operating practices, equally, affect policy decisions. Although the company has several unconventional ways of operating, there is nevertheless an overall harmony.

Summary

Each organisation is unique in some way and must be treated as such. There is no single blueprint for success. To repeat our earlier comments, simply grafting on techniques which work in other situations is unlikely to be the answer. The activities of operations managers cannot be looked at in isolation. 'Operations' is a function of the organisation and as such must not only integrate with the other functions but also be in accord with the situation, objectives and policies of the organisation as a whole.

We hope this book has stimulated you to find out more about operations management and we hope you will pursue your interest not only by further reading, but by direct contact with those involved in operations. Theory and practice go hand in hand.

Further Reading

Standard Texts

Krajewski and Ritzman (1987) Chapter 20.
Schmenner (1987) Chapter 10.

Specialist Texts

Ohmae,K. (1982) *The Mind of the Strategist*, Penguin. An insider's explanation of why Japanese firms have succeeded.
Quinn, J.B. *et al.* (1988) *The Strategy Process,* Prentice Hall. Many authors review the state of the art of business policy as at 1988. Numerous case studies including some fascinating military analogies.

BIBLIOGRAPHY

Operations Management Texts

Adam, E.E. and Ebert, R.J. (1986) *Production and Operations Management: Concepts, Models and Behaviour*, 3rd edn, Prentice Hall. This contains an excellent chapter on forecasting. The main forecasting approaches are explained from first principles, built around a careful discussion of which forecasting model is most appropriate followed by a good set of exercises. The MRP and Quality chapters are similarly good.

Burbidge, J.L. (1971) *The Principles of Production Control*, 3rd edn, Macdonald and Evans. An older book, but still very strong for its combination of practicality and common sense, especially in the systems, scheduling and inventory-control areas. Note that he was neatly, convincingly dismissing Economic Order Quantity twenty years before it became fashionable to do so.

Chase, R.B. and Aquilano, N.J. (1981) *Production and Operations Management. A Life Cycle Approach*, 3rd edn, Irwin. You do not have to go along with their rather oddball 'life cycle' structure to appreciate the many fine features in this book. Their discussion on scheduling is very comprehensive and enlightening − see in particular their synopsis of Sandman's Q-Control.

Delmar, D. (1985) *Operations and Industrial Management*, McGraw-Hill. This contains stimulating chapters on product design, the working environment and industrial espionage.

Dilworth, J.B. (1986) *Production and Operations Management*, 3rd edn, Random. Useful for the historic background (Supplement C), Master Production Schedules, lot sizing in MRP, the exercises set in the Scheduling chapter and the discussion on flexible manufacturing systems.

Evans, J.R. *et al.* (1987) *Applied Production and Operations Management*, 2nd edn, West Publishing Company. Comprehensive book with especially interesting coverage on these topics: CAD, simulation, bar codes, ergonomics, systems design, work measurement, MPS, MRP, OPT, JIT.

Harding, H.A. (1984) *Production Management,* 4th edn, M & E. Includes some clear expositions on machines and the inspection side of quality, bringing out some points that have often been overlooked.

Hill, T. (1983) *Production/Operations Management,* Prentice Hall. Opens with enlightening comments on the role of the operations manager.

Hunter, R. (1983) *Production,* Mitchell Beazley. Neat pocket book, which in spite of its brevity is a useful reference for Value Analysis, Methods Study, simple scheduling and MRP.

Krajewski, L.J. and Ritzman, L.P. (1987) *Operations Management, Strategy and Analysis,* Addison Wesley. Big-budget American blockbuster, orthodox, but with space to devote to new manufacturing technologies and extensions to MRP. Also contains a nice snippet on Toyota's Kanban system.

Lewis, C.D. (1981) *Operations Management in Practice,* Philip Allan. A series of readings mixing introductory and in-depth material. In particular, Chapters 10 and 11 cover certain fundamental costing principles overlooked in the textbooks. There are also enlightening sections on incentive schemes, work measurement, forecasting, inventory control, MRP and quality. But note that the easier discussion often follows the more difficult.

Lockyer, K.G. (1975) *Production Control in Practice,* 2nd edn, Pitman. Nice, clear numerical-forecasting examples, also nice examples of job shop algorithms (e.g. Johnsons). A good summary of material control.

Lockyer, K.G. (1986) *Production Management,* 4th edn, Pitman. An excellent introductory perspective. Don't miss the machine-tool project network stuck in the design chapter. Gives good coverage of several overlooked 'grubby' topics, such as materials handling, store keeping, and health and safety. Some excellent scheduling workouts (don't overlook MPS in Appendix 8) and some wise words on the tactics and strategy of purchasing.

Mayer, R. (1975) *Production and Operations Management,* 3rd edn, McGraw-Hill. Strong on materials handling, inventory-control diagnosis, methods, work measurement, payment schemes. Don't overlook a nice, simple introduction to metal processes in Appendix A.

McLain, J.O. and Thomas, L.J. (1980) *Operations Management,* Prentice Hall. Highlights the importance of often-overlooked general features of trade-off analysis. Contains a very sensible coverage of forecasting, even making some sense out of the mystical Box–Jenkins method. Good on Master Schedules. Don't overlook Appendices A, B, and C which give an excellent lead into queuing and simulation.

Monks, J.G. (1985) *Operations Management, Theory and Problems,* 2nd edn, McGraw-Hill. Interesting on layouts, purchasing, jobs and Master Schedules.

Schmenner, R.W. (1987) *Production/Operations Management, Concepts and Situations,* 3rd edn, SRA. Difficult to get hold of in the UK but a book with many fine sections. Schmenner's original introduction of Plant Tours really gets the reader involved, and his interspersion of short Situation Case Studies in the text also holds the attention. Throughout there is a high standard, but look in particular at his concluding chapter on Operations Strategy and his comparison of the Japanese and American way of doing things.

Stevenson, W.J. (1986) *Production/Operations Management,* 2nd edn, Irwin. Interesting assessment and introduction to forecasting. Neat review of work systems. A more in-depth treatment of MPS than is normal, tying it into an LP formulation. Nice, simple coverage of MRP and JIT.

Books of Case Studies in Operations Management

Constable, C.J. and New, C.C. (1976) *Operations Management, A Systems Approach Through Text and Cases,* Wiley. Enlightening cases to tackle, of which our favourites are: Berger Paints Distribution (vehicle scheduling); Bridge Electric (A) (assembly-line balancing); Bridge Electric (B) (payments system); Winton Shirt Company (quality control).

Meier, R.C. (1982) *Cases in Production and Operations Management,* Prentice Hall. Lots of not-too-long practical cases suitable for class analysis. This is our selection of the best ones: Aerodyne (MPS); Bednap (people problems); Maynard (MPS); Midcentral (forecasting); Ohio (quality assurance); Osburn (work scheduling); Othello (line balancing); Petersen (project planning); Quick-lube (methods, teams, systems); Southern Hydraulic (ROQ/ROL); Teem Aircraft Corporation (purchasing, vendor rating); Transcontinental (machine purchases).

Nicholson, T.A.J. (1978) *Managing Manufacturing Operations, A Casebook,* Macmillan. Classic set of cases giving a 'warts and all' picture of UK manufacturing management. Excellent on the documentary detail and for highlighting problems from the manager's viewpoint. We recommend the following: Micronair (new product development and people); English Steel (material handling); Speedcraft Transport (forecasting); Adams Ice Cream (forecasting); Medina (scheduling); Van Heugten (ROQ/ROL).

Schmenner, R.W. (1986) *Cases in Production/Operations Management,* SRA. Excellent set of cases, with these being our favourites: Carmen Canning Co. (systems); Dayton, Knox (incentives, work measurement); Macpherson (MPS); Lamson (ROQ/ROL); Kumera (scheduling); and The Problem with Kathy (A) and (B) (quality control); Drug Distribution at Victoria Hospital (quality diagnosis); Kalen's (materials control); Dean's Brewery (machines).

INDEX